# AIR T
## RADIO
# FREQUENCIES

**Ken Davies**

IAN ALLAN
*Publishing*

This edition published 1995

ISBN 0 7110 2320 4

Material on aircraft recognition reproduced from *abc Civil Airliner Recognition* and *abc Light Aircraft Recognition* by Peter R. March. Both copyright © Ian Allan Ltd.

Published by Ian Allan Publishing: an imprint of Ian Allan Ltd, Terminal House, Station Approach, Shepperton, Surrey TW17 8AS.

Printed by Ian Allan Printing Ltd, Coombelands House, Coombelands Lane, Addlestone, Surrey KT15 1HY.

**Front cover:**
*Photograph supplied by Steepletone Products Ltd.*

**Back cover:**
PA-28R Cherokee Arrow (G-AWFK) owned by Steepletone Products Ltd.
*Photograph supplied by Steepletone Products Ltd.*

# CONTENTS

AREA MAP ........................................................................................................4

INTRODUCTION.................................................................................................5

ABBREVIATIONS USED IN THIS GUIDE ..........................................................8

IMPORTANT NOTES ON USE OF GUIDE AREAS ...........................................11

HOW TO USE THIS GUIDE ..............................................................................12

AIRFIELDS OF NORTH SCOTLAND – AREA 1..................................................14

ZONES & AIRWAYS OF SCOTLAND – AREAS 1 & 2.........................................16

AIRFIELDS OF SOUTH EAST & WEST SCOTLAND – AREA 2 ..........................17

ZONES & AIRWAYS OF NORTH WEST ENGLAND – AREA 3 ...........................21

AIRFIELDS OF NORTH WEST ENGLAND – AREA 3 ........................................22

ZONES & AIRWAYS OF NW. ENGLAND & IRISH SEA – AREA 4 .....................23

AIRFIELDS OF WEST MIDLANDS & N. WALES – AREA 4 ................................24

ZONES & AIRWAYS OF THE WEST MIDLANDS – AREA 5 ..............................27

AIRFIELDS OF THE MIDLANDS & THAMES VALLEY – AREA 5 ......................28

ZONES & AIRWAYS OF SOUTH MIDLANDS & SOUTH WALES – AREA 5A..............31

AIRFIELDS OF UPPER THAMES VALLEY, SEVERN VALLEY &
    SOUTH WALES – AREA 5A ........................................................................33

OFFSHORE OIL & GAS FIELD RELATED FREQUENCIES.................................36

ZONES & AIRWAYS OF NORTH EAST ENGLAND – AREA 6 ...........................40

AIRFIELDS OF NORTH EASTERN COUNTIES – AREA 6 .................................41

ZONES & AIRWAYS OF HUMBERSIDE & LINCS – AREA 7 .............................45

AIRFIELDS OF HUMBERSIDE, EAST MIDLANDS & LINCS – AREA 7 .............46

ZONES & AIRWAYS OF EAST MIDLANDS – AREA 8 .......................................49

AIRFIELDS OF COUNTIES NORTH OF LONDON – AREA 8 .............................50

ZONES & AIRWAYS NORTH EAST OF LONDON – AREA 8A ...........................52

AIRFIELDS OF ANGLIA & COUNTIES NORTH EAST OF LONDON – AREA 8A.....54

ZONES & AIRWAYS OF LONDON & SOUTH EAST ENGLAND – AREAS 9 & 9A........57

AIRFIELDS OF HOME COUNTIES & GREATER LONDON – AREA 9 .................59

AIRFIELDS OF HOME COUNTIES SOUTH OF LONDON &
    CENTRAL SOUTH COAST – AREA 9A.........................................................61

ZONES & AIRWAYS OF SOUTH WESTERN ENGLAND & CHANNEL ISLANDS
    – AREAS 10 & 10A......................................................................................66

AIRFIELDS OF SOUTH WESTERN COUNTIES – AREA 10...............................67

AIRFIELDS OF DEVON, CORNWALL & CHANNEL ISLANDS – AREA 10A.................69

AIRFIELDS OF NORTHERN & SOUTHERN IRELAND – AREA 11 ....................72

COMMUNICATION COMMON FREQUENCIES ................................................76

AIRCRAFT RECOGNITION SECTION ...............................................................78

# AREA MAP

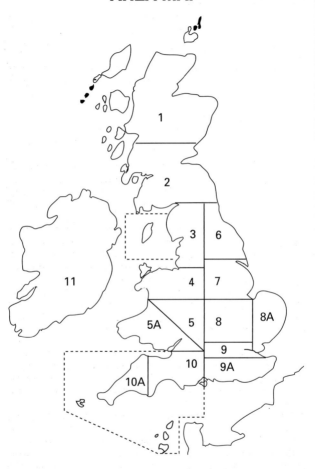

# INTRODUCTION

On looking back over previous editions of my airband guides it looks as if the standard introduction for each one has had to be to apologise for the number of alterations and additions necessary to keep up with the times. Such is the price of advancing technology!

Therefore it will come as no surprise that this edition has to conform to what has become a conventional opening especially so in the coming twelve months. As the new Air Traffic Control Centre at Bursledon is brought on stream the effect this is going to have on the UK Air Traffic Control data given in this guide requires some explanation.

The reasons for the major changes in the system can be summed up in a few simple paragraphs and while these are bound to be a little over simplified they do explain why.

The old centre at West Drayton has been in existence for a quarter of a century during which period the equipment and the actual system of control has become out of date several times. Now it has quite simply reached saturation and expansion has to be allowed for if safety standards and easy working with Eurocontrol centres is to happen.

There is a much needed bonus that this new centre makes possible, that of the ability to increase the capacity to handle some 30% more traffic with even greater safety, and nobody is going to argue with that! Again, at the risk of over simplification one of the changes in the system that makes these desirable features possible is to alter the 'airways concept'.

The system in use up to now has been to designate a path through the airspace in a designated 'Airway' some ten miles wide and several thousand feet from top to bottom. Each of these 'Airways' have a controller to regulate and control the traffic in each sector of the individual 'airlanes'. Aircraft using these airlanes do so under the control of a sector controller.

He ensures that the aircraft in his sector conform to the 'rules of the road'. In general terms these allow for all aircraft flying in one direction along an airway to fly at odd numbers of one thousand feet and those flying in the opposite direction to fly at even numbers of a thousand feet which maintains vertical separation.

Further separation is maintained laterally by the controller designating speed and again normally the aircraft in an airlane fly in one direction to the left of the lanes centre line and those in the opposite direction to the right.

This concept can be likened to a dual carriageway road with crossings and junction controlled by traffic lights and or roundabouts. The new concept is more like a motorway with no stopping and joining traffic joining the flow in one direction. What is being done is in effect to have two parallel 'airways', one for each direction.

This will make it possible to have controllers work load reduced in that although they will have larger sectors they will only have to contend with traffic going in one direction with the resultant safety factors possible with the increased traffic flow.

In a similar way to the method employed by British Telecom to make possible the increase in telephone capacity into the next century by phasing the system over to the new one over a period and then when it is all ready saying the official day, so the Air Traffic system will have to be proven stage by stage and then at some date in the not too distant future the system will be complete. This will take some time and involve changes in control frequencies being phased in over a period which is a situation we are trying to cover by making some alterations in the presentation of data in this guide.

It is my intention to retain the popular geographical format, but the main changes will be to reduce the detail of the designated frequencies. The frequencies controlling overflights and airways will be grouped into the arbitrary areas used in this guide and not listed under the individual airways as before.

Lower and middle Airspace Radar channels will also be grouped in the book areas and the UHF frequencies formally used by military airfields about to close will also be left out of this edition.

However, the common VHF frequencies used for specific purposes nationally both in civil and military aviation will be retained in a clearly designated manner by our geographical format. To make the use of the guide more flexible a limited number of sections are included which for instance give 'common frequencies' such as those used by most of the RAF 'Towers'.

Another slight change made to make the guide more useful in the coming year or so is to provide adequate blank amendment pages so that users may make note of those changes that are likely to affect their usage.

Unfortunately it is not possible to include all the changes that will be made during the year for the simple reason that most of them will not be known or published when we go to print and will be phased in over the life of this edition.

Lead time between finishing typescripts and getting the guide into the bookshops is another factor which inhibits being absolutely up to date when a guide of this type leaves the publishers who have to do their best to keep the cover price of the publication down .

However, having been the compiler of this particular guide for nearly twenty years and now retired from the publishing side of the business I have been lucky to arrange with Ian Allan Ltd. to take over future editions. I am sure this will enable a better distribution to be available and also has the great bonus that they also publish an aviation magazine which will be able to include updates as and when they become available in a format that will enable guide users to keep their amendment pages updated themselves.

Every effort is made to keep up with technology and the data needed to utilise the ever increasing information available. The sophisticated receiving equipment now on sale to the general public has resulted in them being more and more aware of what is possible. For this reason I have left the technicalities of Air to Ground communications to other authors better qualified to describe them and confined this edition to presenting the data in directory form in which the information required is simple to find and easy to use.

However, as usual I have to wind up my introduction with two warnings.

The first being that the compiler and the publishers have made every effort to ensure that the data is accurate at the time of going to press, but cannot be held responsible for errors and omissions that occur for reasons mentioned above. For this reason the guide should not be used for navigational purposes without reference to 'Notams'.

The other regular warning is that of the legality of the use of communication equipment. There is certainly nothing illegal in the publishing of data such as that contained in this guide for it is in the public domain for all to see. What is definitely illegal is the criminal use of information heard, its disclosure to a third party and possibly the use of licensed or unlicensed equipment where it interferes with authorised services.

In this country it seems that common sense prevails and unless a nuisance is created, or a criminal act committed the authorities turn a blind eye to the use of most airband receivers. However, this is not so in some other countries including many of those we regard as friendly, especially if you are using such equipment near a military installation. So, if in doubt ask first and you will prevent yourself landing up behind bars. I see I am now finishing as I did in a previous edition with these warnings ringing in your ears, be careful, use discretion and enjoy our guide.


**Ken Davies**
Hampshire, 1995

# ABBREVIATIONS USED IN THIS GUIDE

| ABBREVIATION | REMARKS |
| --- | --- |
| A/C | AIRCRAFT |
| ACC | AREA CONTROL CENTRE |
| AFIS | AERODROME FLIGHT INFORMATION SERVICE |
| AG RADIO | AIR TO GROUND RADIO. NORMALLY FOR INFORMATION ONLY AND NOT GIVING MANDATORY INSTRUCTIONS. |
| AM | AMPLITUDE MODULATION. A TYPE OF RADIO TRANSMISSION. |
| APP | APPROACH |
| ARR/Arr | ARRIVALS |
| ATCC | AIR TRAFFIC CONTROL CENTRE |
| ATIS | AUTOMATIC TERMINAL INFORMATION SERVICE |
| ATZ | AERODROME TRAFFIC ZONE |
| BDY | BOUNDARY |
| CAS | CONTROLLED AIRSPACE |
| CIV AF | CIVIL AIRFIELD. CAN VARY FROM LARGE AIRFIELD WITH OR WITHOUT HARD RUNWAYS TO ONE OR MORE GRASS STRIPS NORMALLY LICENSED. |
| CIV AP | MAJOR AIRPORT WITH SUBSTANTIAL NUMBER OF SCHEDULED SERVICES AND NAVIGATIONAL AIDS. |
| CTA | CONTROL AREA |
| CTR | CONTROL ZONE |
| DEP/dep | DEPARTURES |
| DIR | DIRECTOR |
| DME | DISTANCE MEASURING EQUIPMENT |
| DZ | DROPPING ZONE FOR PARACHUTING |
| FIR | FLIGHT INFORMATION REGION |
| FIS | FLIGHT INFORMATION SERVICE |
| FL | FLIGHT LEVEL |
| FLTS | FLIGHTS |
| FM | FREQUENCY MODULATION. A TYPE OF RADIO TRANSMISSION. |
| FREQ | FREQUENCY |
| GMC | GROUND MOVEMENT CONTROL |
| GMD | GROUND MOVEMENT CONTROL |
| GRND | GROUND MOVEMENT CONTROL |
| HELI | HELICOPTER |
| HELIPAD | HELICOPTER PAD |
| HF | HIGH FREQUENCY. TYPE OF RADIO TRANSMISSION. |
| HRS | HOURS |
| 1FR | INSTRUMENT FLIGHT RULES |

| ABBREVIATION | REMARKS |
|---|---|
| ILS | INSTRUMENT LANDING SYSTEM |
| IMC | INSTRUMENT METEOROLOGICAL CONDITIONS |
| INFO | INFORMATION |
| INTL | INTERNATIONAL |
| KHz | KILOHERTZ (RADIO FREQUENCY MEASUREMENT) |
| LARS | LOWER AIRSPACE RADAR ADVISORY SERVICE |
| LJAO | LONDON JOINT AREA ORGANISATION |
| MACC | MILITARY AREA CONTROL CENTRE |
| MARS | MIDDLE AIRSPACE RADAR ADVISORY SERVICE |
| MATZ | MILITARY AERODROME TRAFFIC ZONE |
| MEDA | MILITARY EMERGENCY DIVERSION AERODROME |
| METRO | PILOT TO METRO VOICE |
| MHz | MEGAHERTZ (RADIO FREQUENCY MEASUREMENT) |
| MIL | MILITARY |
| MIL AF | MILITARY AIRFIELD. (VARIES FROM MAJOR AIRFIELD TO HELICOPTER PAD) |
| MOD | MINISTRY OF DEFENCE |
| MRSA | MANDATORY RADAR SERVICE AREA |
| NDB | NON DIRECTIONAL BEACON |
| OAC | OCEANIC AREA CONTROL |
| OACC | OCEANIC AREA CONTROL CENTRE |
| OPS | OPERATIONS |
| OR | ON REQUEST |
| PAR | PRECISION APPROACH RADAR (TALKDOWN) |
| PAR RADAR | PRECISION APPROACH RADAR (TALKDOWN) |
| PRI | PRIVATE |
| PRI AF | PRIVATE AIRFIELD. CAN VARY FROM MAJOR AIRFIELD SUCH AS WARTON DOWN TO A SINGLE GRASS FARM STRIP. |
| RAD | RADAR |
| REG | REGISTERED |
| RNWY | RUNWAY |
| SAR | SEARCH AND RESCUE |
| SOTA | SHANNON OCEANIC TRANSITION AREA |
| SRA or SRZ | AIRSPACE IN WHICH SPECIAL RULES APPLY |
| SRE | SURVEILLANCE RADAR ELEMENT |
| SSB | SINGLE SIDE BAND. A TYPE OF RADIO TRANSMISSION. |
| STN | STATION. USUALLY REFERS TO RADIO STATION, BUT COULD MEAN RAF AIRFIELD. |
| TCA | TERMINAL CONTROL AREA |
| TMA | TERMINAL CONTROL AREA |
| TWR | TOWER |
| UAS | UPPER AIRSPACE SERVICE |
| UHF | ULTRA HIGH FREQUENCY. TYPE OF RADIO TRANSMISSION. |
| UIR | UPPER INFORMATION REGION |
| UIS | UPPER INFORMATION SERVICE |

| ABBREVIATION | REMARKS |
|---|---|
| VFR | VISUAL FLIGHT RULES |
| VHF | VERY HIGH FREQUENCY. TYPE OF RADIO TRANSMISSION. |
| VMC | VISUAL METEOROLOGICAL CONDITIONS |
| VOLMET | METEOROLOGICAL INFORMATION FOR AIRCRAFT IN FLIGHT |
| VOR | VHF OMNIDIRECTIONAL RANGE (VHF BEACON) |

## IMPORTANT NOTE

*THE AREAS USED IN THIS GUIDE ARE FOR CONVENIENCE OF DISPLAYING INFORMATION AND SHOULD NOT BE REGARDED AS ACCURATE AND NEVER USED FOR NAVIGATION*

# IMPORTANT NOTES ON USE OF GUIDE AREAS

1) DATA THAT REFERS TO THE SERVICE AT EACH STATION IS AS UP TO DATE AS CAN BE ASCERTAINED TO THE END OF 1994. WE REGRET THAT THE COMPILER AND THE PUBLISHER CAN NOT BE RESPONSIBLE FOR ERRORS OR OMISSIONS CAUSED BY ALTERATIONS MADE BETWEEN THE TIME DATA BECAME AVAILABLE TO THEM AND THE TIME OF GOING TO PRINT.

2) THE AREAS USED IN THIS GUIDE ARE PURELY ARBITRARY TO ALLOW THE GUIDE USER TO LOCATE MOST SERVICES AVAILABLE IN THE AREAS TO BE LOCATED IN ADJACENT SECTIONS OR PAGES.

3) AN AMENDMENT PAGE IS PROVIDED AT THE END OF EACH AREA SECTION HEADED IN THE WAY OTHER SECTOR DATA IS PRESENTED TO ENABLE THE GUIDE USER TO MAKE THEIR OWN UPDATES AS THEY COME TO HAND.

4) THAT THE SERVICE LISTED (EG. AN APPROACH OR RADAR FREQUENCY MAY NOT BE AVAILABLE ON A 24 HOUR BASIS, OR EVEN EVERY DAY). IN SOME CASES THIS APPLIES TO WHOLE AIRFIELDS, ESPECIALLY THE SMALL PRIVATELY OWNED AIRSTRIPS AND WORKS OWNED FIELDS.

5) TACTICAL MILITARY UHF TRANSMISSIONS AND MOST PRIVATE BUSINESS FREQUENCIES HAVE BEEN OMITTED TO AVOID REPERCUSSIONS THAT MIGHT OCCUR BECAUSE OF MISUSE OF THE INFORMATION TRANSMITTED AND ALSO THESE DO CHANGE MORE FREQUENTLY THAN OTHER SERVICES.

# HOW TO USE THIS GUIDE

The map opposite divides the country into arbitrary areas and has taken a few minor liberties with geography. However, the purpose of this is to obtain a logical system of reference which enables anyone with an interest in the 'Airband Communications Frequencies' to find in the guide those that can be received in whatever part of the UK they happen to be in.

There will inevitably be some overlap and with freak reception conditions that prevail from time to time. On some occasions those frequencies listed will not be received when one expects to do so and others when some channels you don't expect will come in loud and clear.

In the normal course of events, if you are within a mile or so of an airfield, then you will be able to hear transmission to and from that field, but at a greater distance you will normally only hear the aircraft as well as most of the overflight and transmissions that are used for the airways and zone controls for that particular area.

In most cases a call from an overflight will be heard, but if you are not close to the ground station called you will only hear the aircraft and not the ground station's reply. This is because all VHF and UHF transmissions under normal conditions are line of sight, so it will be realised that the higher the aircraft transmitting is, the further the transmission will travel and so be heard.

As far as possible the pages have been arranged so that most of the transmissions that can be received from a particular place are within a couple of pages from the situation the listener happens to be in. This means that it is not necessary to flick from page to page to find the frequency that interests you.

To sum up, decide which area you are in from the map on the previous page, turn to the page that serves the area you are in and select the frequencies you wish to hear. *Good Listening!*

# DISCLAIMER

It has been mentioned in the introduction that in these last two years there seem to have been more alterations in frequency channels than ever before in one given period.

It would seem that the reasons for all these changes are mainly concerned with the cut back of some military installations, changes brought about by the rationalisation made possible with the ending of the so-called 'Cold War', the use of UHF channels for company communications and the allocation of new frequencies utilising the extra bandwidth available because of the introduction of more and more equipment with 12.5 kHz spacing.

The above factors have made it possible to be absolutely up to date no matter what time you go to press with what is, in effect, a 'year book' type of directory. For this reason the publishers are leaving space for users to pencil in such additions and deletions as users become aware of them.

By adopting this policy it is possible to maintain the guide within a price bracket that is affordable by enthusiasts and commercial users alike.

# AREA MAP

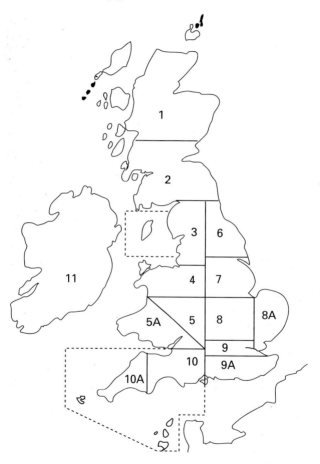

# AREA 1

## AIRFIELDS OF NORTH SCOTLAND

| STATION | TYPE | FREQUENCY | SERVICE / REMARKS / CALL |
|---|---|---|---|
| UNST | CIV AP | 130.35 | TWR / APP |
| | | 123.45 | OPS |
| | | 123.15 | SUMBURGH RADAR |
| LERWICK (TINGWALL) | 122.6 | TWR / AG | PRI AF |
| SCATSCA | PRI AF | 123,6 | TWR / APP |
| | | 122.4 | RADAR |
| | | 121.6 | FIRE |
| FAIR ISLE | CIV AF | 123.15 | SUMBURGH APP |
| WHALSAY | CIV AF | 123.15 | SUMBURGH APP |
| SUMBURGH | CIV AP | 118.25 | TWR |
| | | 125.85 | ATIS |
| | | 123.15 | APP |
| | | 123.15 | RAD |
| | | 130.05 | RAD |
| | | 118.15 | RAD |
| NORTH RONALDSAY | CIV AF | 118.3 | KIRKWALL APP |
| EDAY | CIV AF | 118.3 | KIRKWALL APP |
| PAPA WESTRAY | CIV AF | 118.3 | KIRKWALL APP |
| WESTRAY | CIV AP | 118.3 | KIRKWALL APP |
| SANDAY | CIV AP | 118.3 | KIRKWALL APP |
| STRONSAY | CIV AP | 118.3 | KIRKWALL APP |
| KIRKWALL | CIV AP | 118.3 | TWR / APP |
| FLOTTA | PRI AF | 122.15 | AG RADIO |
| STORNAWAY | CIV AP | 123.5 | TWR / APP |
| | | 123.5 | AFIS OUT OF TWR HRS |
| | | 362.3 | APP |
| WICK | CIV AP | 119.7 | TWR |
| | | 130.37 | FAR NORTH AG |
| INVERNESS | CIV AP | 122.6 | TWR / APP |
| | | 121.6 | FIRE |
| | | 362.3 | APP |
| TAIN RANGE | MIL RANGE | 122.75 | MIL RANGE AG |
| GARVIE | MIL RANGE | 133.2 | MIL RANGE AG |

# AREA 1

## AIRFIELDS OF NORTH SCOTLAND

| STATION | TYPE | FREQUENCY | SERVICE / REMARKS / CALL |
|---|---|---|---|
| **FEARN** | PRI AF | 122.75 | TAIN RANGE RADIO |
| **KINLOSS** | MIL AF | 122.1 | TWR |
| | | 119.35 | APP / MATZ |
| | | 123.3 | DIRECTOR |
| | | 123.3 | DIR / PAR RAD / SRE |
| | | *336.35* | *TWR* |
| | | *257.8* | *TWR* |
| | | *376.65* | *APP* |
| | | *362.3* | *APP* |
| | | *358.475* | *OPS* |
| | | *259.075* | *DIR* |
| | | *311.325* | *DIR* |
| | | *370.05* | *PAR RADAR* |
| | | *376.525* | *PAR RADAR* |
| **DORNOCH** | PRI AF | 119.35 | LOSSIEMOUTH APP |
| **LOSSIEMOUTH** | MIL AF | 118.9 | TWR |
| | | 122.1 | TWR |
| | | 119.35 | APP / MATZ / LARS |
| | | 123.3 | APP |
| | | 123.3 | PAR RADAR |
| | | *337.75* | *TWR* |
| | | *299.4* | *GRND* |
| | | *376.65* | *APP /LARS* |
| | | *362.3* | *APP* |
| | | *258.85* | *DEPARTURES* |
| | | *259.975* | *DIR* |
| | | *311.325* | *DIR* |
| | | *250.05* | *PAR RADAR* |
| | | *312.4* | *PAR RADAR* |
| **INSCH** | PRI AF | 129.825 | AG RADIO |
| | | 120.4 | ABERDEEN APP |
| ***ABERDEEN*** | CIV AP | 118.1 | TWR |
| | | 121.7 | GRND |
| | | 114.3 | ATIS (ARRIVAL INFO) |
| | | 121.85 | ATIS (DEPARTURE INFO) |
| | | 120.4 | APP (NORTH SEA RAD) |
| | | 128.3 | NORTH SEA RADAR |
| | | 121.25 | NORTH SEA RADAR |
| | | 353.55 | APP / NORTH SEA RADAR |

# AREAS 1 & 2

## ZONES & AIRWAYS OF SCOTLAND

| FREQUENCY | CALL | SERVICE |
|-----------|------|---------|
| 119.0 | EAST SHETLAND BASIN | ATIS |
| 129.95 | VIKING APP | HELI FIS |
| 122.25 | BRENT | APP |
| 130.2 | NINIAN | APP |
| 118.5 | SAXA VORD | SHETLAND RADAR |
| 118.15 | SUMBURG RADAR | SHETLAND RADAR |
| 134.15 | | SHETLAND RADAR |
| 134.1 | | HIGHLAND RADAR (CIV) |
| 126.1 | | HIGHLAND RADAR (AS DIR) |
| 131.3 | SCOTTISH INFORMATION | NORTH OF FIR |
| 127.275 | SCOTTISH INFORMATION | WEST OF FIR |
| 119.875 | SCOTTISH INFORMATION | SOUTH OF FIR |
| 134.3 | SCOTTISH MIL | RADAR & INFORMATION |
| 249.475 | SCOTTISH MIL | INCLUDING SCOTTISH MRSA |
| 125.725 | SCOTTISH VOLMET | BROADCAST WEATHER SERVICE |
| 133.875 | PENNINE RADAR | |
| 128.675 | PENNINE RADAR | |
| 126.25 | SCOTTISH CONTROL | AIRWAYS—A1, A2, A25, |
| 123.375 | SCOTTISH CONTROL | AIRWAYS—A1, A2, A25, |
| 124.5 | SCOTTISH CONTROL | AIRWAYS—B2, B226, W3D, W911D, |
| 126.85 | SCOTTISH CONTROL | AIRWAYS—B2, B3, B4, W911D, W928D, |
| 127.275 | SCOTTISH CONTROL | AIRWAYS—A1D, N552D, N562D, N571D, W6D, W985D |
| 131.3 | SCOTTISH CONTROL | AIRWAYS—B1D, W3D, W4D, W5D, W6D, |
| 125.675 | SCOTTISH CONTROL | AIRWAYS—UH73, UN517, UN537, UN545, UN550, UN551, UN552, UN559, UN560, UN561, UN562, UN563, UN564, UN569, UN570, UN571, UN572, UN573, UN580, UN590, UN601, UN602, UN615, UR38. |
| 135.85 | SCOTTISH CONTROL | AIRWAYS—UA1, UA2, UA25, UB2, UB3, UB4, UB5, UH73, UN537, UN545, UN550, UN551, UN552, UN559, UN560, UN561, UN562, UN563, UN564, UN569, UN570, UN571, UN572, UN573, UN580, UN580, UN615, UR23, UR38. |
| 133.675 | SCOTTISH CONTROL | AIRWAYS—UB2, UG11, UH70, UH71, UH73, UL7, UN517, UN580, UN581, UN583, UN584, UN590, UN591, |

| | | | |
|---|---|---|---|
| 134.775 | SCOTTISH CONTROL | | UN593, UN601, UN602, UN603, UN610, UN611, UN612, UN615, UR38. AIRWAYS—UH70, UH71, UG11, UL7, UR38, UN584, UN590, UN591, UN593, UN601, UN602, UN603, UN610, UN611, UN612, UN615, UR23, |

# AREA 2

## AIRFIELDS OF SOUTH EAST OF SCOTLAND

| STATION | TYPE | FREQUENCY | SERVICE / REMARKS / CALL |
|---|---|---|---|
| **PERTH (SCONE)** | CIV AF | 119.8 | TWR |
| | | 122.3 | APP |
| **DUNDEE** | CIV AF | 122.9 | TWR / APP |
| **ERROL** | PRI AF | 123.45 | DZ CONTROL ERROL |
| | | 122.3 | PERTH APP |
| | | 126.5 | LEUCHARS APP |
| | | 122.9 | DUNDEE APP |
| **KINROSS** | PRI AF | 119.875 | SCOTTISH INFORMATION |
| **FIFE (GLENROTHES)** | CIV AF | 130.45 | AG RADIO |
| **LEUCHARS** | MIL AF | 122.1 | TWR |
| | | 126.5 | APP / MATZ / LARS |
| | | 123.3 | PAR / DIR / SRE |
| | | 258.925 | *TWR / GRND* |
| | | *362.3* | *APP* |
| | | 255.4 | *APP / MATZ / LARS* |
| | | *285.025* | *OPS* |
| | | *292.475* | *DIR* |
| | | *370.075* | *PAR RADAR* |
| | | *268.775* | *PAR RADAR* |
| **LEITH HELIPAD** | CIV PAD | 122.5 | AG RADIO |
| | | 121.2 | EDINBURGH APP |
| *EDINBURGH* | CIV AP | 118.7 | TWR / APP |
| | | 121.75 | GRND |
| | | 132.075 | ATIS |
| | | 121.2 | APP / RAD |
| | | 130.4 | FOR GLIDERS IN ATZ |
| | | 128.975 | APP AS DIRECTED |
| | | 121.2 | RAD |
| | | 121.6 | FIRE |
| | | *257.8* | *TWR / GRND* |
| | | *362.3* | *RADAR* |

# AREA 2

## AIRFIELDS OF WEST OF SCOTLAND

| STATION | TYPE | FREQUENCY | SERVICE / REMARKS / CALL |
|---|---|---|---|
| ST KILDA | MIL PAD | 128.1 | AG RADIO |
| BENBECULA | CIV AP | 119.2 | TWR / APP / AFIS |
| BARRA | CIV AP | 130.65 | AG RADIO / LOGANAIR |
| ISLE OF SKYE (BROADFORD) | CIV AP | 130.65 | AG RADIO / LOGANAIR |
| PLOCKTON | CIV AF | 122.375 | AG RADIO |
| KYLE (RN) | MIL RANGE | 130.65 | AG RADIO |
| TIREE | CIV AP | 122.7 | AFIS |
| COLONSAY (MACHRINS) | CIV AF | 122.7 | TIREE INFORMATION |
| COLL (BALLARD) | PRI AF | 122.7 | TIREE INFORMATION |
| GLENFORSA (MULL) | CIV AF | 124.5 | SCOTTISH INFORMATION |
| OBAN | CIV AF | 130.1<br>129.825 | AG RADIO (GLIDERS)<br>AG (MICROLIGHTS) |
| GIGHA | PRI AF | 123.05<br>125.9 | AG RADIO<br>MACHRIOHANISH APP |
| ISLAY | CIV AP | 123.15 | AFIS. (ISLAY INFO) |
| STRATHALLAN | PRI AF | 129.9 | AG RADIO |
| CUMBERNAULD | CIV AF | 120.6 | AG RADIO / AFIS |
| GLASGOW | CIV AP | 118.8<br>121.7<br>115.4<br>119.1<br>119.3<br>121.3<br>121.6<br>362.3 | TWR<br>GRND<br>ATIS (ARR / DEP INFO)<br>APP / RAD<br>RAD<br>RAD<br>FIRE<br>APP / RAD |
| GLASGOW CITY HELIPORT | CIV HELIPA | 119.1 | GLASGOW APP |
| PRESTWICK | CIV AP | 118.15<br>121.8<br>121.8<br>127.125<br>120.55<br>119.45 | TWR<br>TWR<br>GRND<br>ATIS<br>APP / RAD<br>RAD |

# AREA 2

## AIRFIELDS OF WEST OF SCOTLAND

| STATION | TYPE | FREQUENCY | SERVICE / REMARKS / CALL |
|---|---|---|---|
| **PRESTWICK (Continued)** | | 121.6 | FIRE |
| | | 9013 KHz | RN PRESTWICK HF SSB |
| | | *337.75* | *RN. PRESTWICK* |
| **SHANWICK RADIO (OCEANIC CONTROL)** | | | |
| NAT A. | ALL AIRCRAFT: | 3016 KHz | SOUTHERN ROUTES |
| | | 5598 KHz | SOUTHERN ROUTES |
| | | 8906 KHz | SOUTHERN ROUTES |
| | | 13306 KHz | SOUTHERN ROUTES |
| | | 17946 KHz | SOUTHERN ROUTES |
| NAT B. | A/C REG W. OF 30 W. | 2899 KHz | NORTH & CEN ROUTES |
| | | 5616 KHz | NORTH & CEN ROUTES |
| | | 8864 KHz | NORTH & CEN ROUTES |
| | | 13291 KHz | NORTH & CEN ROUTES |
| | | 17946 KHz | NORTH & CEN ROUTES |
| NAT C. | A/C REG E. OF 30 W. | 2872 KHz | NORTH & CEN ROUTES |
| | | 5649 KHz | NORTH & CEN ROUTES |
| | | 8879 KHz | NORTH & CEN ROUTES |
| | | 11336 KHz | NORTH & CEN ROUTES |
| | | 13306 KHz | NORTH & CEN ROUTES |
| | | 17946 KHz | NORTH & CEN ROUTES |
| NAT D. | A/C OUTSIDE OTS ROUTES | 2971 KHz | POLAR ROUTES |
| | | 4675 KHz | POLAR ROUTES |
| | | 8891 KHz | POLAR ROUTES |
| | | 11279 KHz | POLAR ROUTES |
| | | 13291 KHz | POLAR ROUTES |
| | | 17946 KHz | POLAR ROUTES |
| NAT F. | ALL AIRCRAFT | 3376 KHz | CENTRAL ROUTES |
| | | 6622 KHz | CENTRAL ROUTES |
| | | 8831 KHz | CENTRAL ROUTES |
| | | 13291 KHz | CENTRAL ROUTES |
| | | 17946 KHz | CENTRAL ROUTES |
| **MACHRIHANISH** | MIL AF | 122.1 | TWR / APP |
| | | 125.9 | APP/ DIR / SRE |
| | | 123.3 | PAR RADAR |
| | | *358.6* | *TWR* |
| | | *257.8* | *TWR* |
| | | *344.525* | *APP* |
| | | *382.3* | *APP* |
| | | *337.925* | *PAR RADAR* |
| | | *385.4* | *PAR RADAR* |

# AREA 2

## AIRFIELDS OF WEST OF SCOTLAND

| STATION | TYPE | FREQUENCY | SERVICE / REMARKS / CALL |
|---|---|---|---|
| **WEST FREUGH** | MOD AF | 122.55 | TWR |
| | | 130.05 | APP / RAD / MATZ |
| | | 130.725 | RAD |
| | | 337.925 | TWR |
| | | *383.525* | *APP / RAD* |
| | | *259.0* | *RAD / SRE* |
| **WIGTON (BALDOON)** | PRI AF | 123.05 | AG RADIO |

# AMENDMENTS

| STATION | TYPE | FREQUENCY | SERVICE / REMARKS / CALL |
|---|---|---|---|

# AREA 3

## ZONES & AIRWAYS OF NORTH WEST ENGLAND

| FREQUENCY | CALL | SERVICE |
|---|---|---|
| 124.5 | | NORTHERN RADAR ADVISORY |
| 121.5 | | EMERGENCY THROUGH ATCC |
| 243.0 | | EMERGENCY THROUGH ATCC |
| 126.25 | SCOTTISH CONTROL | AIRWAYS—A1, A25 |
| 123.357 | SCOTTISH CONTROL | AIRWAYS—A1, A2, A25, B4 |
| 126.85 | SCOTTISH CONTROL | AIRWAYS—B2, B3, B4, |
| 123.375 | SCOTTISH CONTROL | ENTERING TMA FROM SOUTH EAST |
| 126.25 | SCOTTISH CONTROL | ENTERING TMA FROM SOUTH WEST |
| 125.725 | VOLMET BROADCAST | SCOTTISH VOLMET |
| 131.3 | SCOTTISH INFORMATION | NORTH OF FIR |
| 127.275 | SCOTTISH INFORMATION | WEST OF FIR |
| 119.875 | SCOTTISH INFORMATION | SOUTH OF FIR |
| 134.3 | SCOTTISH MIL | RADAR & INFORMATION |
| 275.475 | SCOTTISH MIL | RADAR & INFORMATION |
| 128.425 | BORDER RADAR | UAS & TRANSIT |
| 133.875 | BORDER RADAR | UAS, MARS & TRANSIT |
| 134.7 | LONDON INFORMATION | NORTH OF FIR |
| 128.7 | LONDON MIL (NORTH) | RADAR & INFORMATION |
| 231.625 | LONDON MIL (IRISH SEA) | RADAR & INFORMATION |
| 231.625 | LONDON MIL | NW & IRISH SEA |
| 126.6 | VOLMET BROADCAST | VOLMET NORTH |
| 135.375 | VOLMET BROADCAST | VOLMET MAIN |
| 127.0 | VOLMET BROADCAST | DUBLIN VOLMET (IRISH SEA) |
| 121.025 | LONDON CONTROL | AIRWAYS—A2, A20, A30, A47, B3, B4, R41, UA2, UB3, UB4, UA47, UB317, UR41. |
| 126.875 | LONDON CONTROL | AIRWAYS—A1, A25, B4, R3, R101, W927D, UAI, UA2, UA25, UB4, UB1, UR4. |
| 128.05 | LONDON CONTROL | AIRWAYS—A25, B3, B1, B53, B39. R3, W2D, W927D, UA34, UB1. |
| 129.1 | LONDON CONTROL | AIRWAYS—A1, A25, B3, B1, R3, R101, W2D, W927D, UA1, UA2, UA25, UA34, UA251. |
| 132.9 | BORDER RADAR | AIRWAYS—W911D, |
| 131.05 | LONDON CONTROL | AIRWAYS—A1, A2, A20, A47, B1, B4, R101, UA1, UA2, UA25, UA251, UB1, UB4, UR4. |
| 134.25 | LONDON CONTROL | AIRWAYS—B1, B5, UA37, UB1, UB5, UB105, UL7, UL74, UR4. |
| 134.425 | LONDON CONTROL | AIRWAYS—A1, A2, A25, B1, B4, R3, R101, W2D, W927D, UAI, UA2, UA25, UB1, UB4, UR3, UR4, |

| | | | |
|---|---|---|---|
| 136.2 | LONDON CONTROL | AIRWAYS—A1, A2, A20, A47, B1, R101, W2D, UA1, UA2, UB4. | |
| 124.2 | MANCHESTER ACC | AIRWAYS BELOW FL 155—A1, A2, A20, A47, B1, B3, B4, R3, R101, W2D, B53 | |
| 125.1 | MANCHESTER ACC | AIRWAYS BELOW FL 155—A25, B1, B3, R3, W911D, B53, | |
| 133.05 | MANCHESTER ACC | AIRWAYS BELOW FL 155—A25, B1, B3, W2D, W927D, | |
| 126.65 | MANCHESTER ACC | AIRWAYS BELOW FL 155—A1, A2, A20, A47, B1, B4, R101, W2D, | |

NOTE:- MANCHESTER SUB CENTRE CONTROLS APPROACH TO MANCHESTER INTERNATIONAL AIRPORT AND AIRWAYS BELOW FLIGHT LEVEL 175 IN ZONE.

# AREA 3

## AIRFIELDS OF NORTH WEST ENGLAND

| STATION | TYPE | FREQUENCY | SERVICE / REMARKS / CALL |
|---|---|---|---|
| **SPADEADAM RANGE** | MIL RANGE | 122.1 | AG RADIO |
| | | *369.15* | *AG RADIO* |
| **KIRKBRIDE** | PRI AF | 123.6 | CARLISLE APP |
| **CARLISLE** | CIV AP | 123.6 | TWR / APP |
| **BARROW (WALNEY)** | PRI AF | 123.2 | TWR / AG RADIO |
| **CARK** | PRI AF | 123.45 | AG RADIO |
| **BLACKPOOL** | CIV AP | 118.4 | TWR |
| | | 135.95 | APP / ATZ |
| | | 119.95 | RAD / SRE |
| **WARTON** | PRI AF | 1380.8 | TWR / APP |
| | | 124.45 | APP / RAD / MATZ / LARS |
| | | 129.725 | APP / RAD |
| | | *311.3* | *TWR / APP / RAD* |
| | | *336.475* | *APP / RAD / MATZ / LARS* |
| | | *343.7* | *RAD / SRE* |
| **RONALDSWAY (I O M)** | CIV AP | 118.9 | TWR / APP |
| | | 120.85 | APP / RAD / LARS |
| | | 118.2 | RAD |
| | | 125.3 | RAD |
| | | 121.6 | FIRE |
| WOODVALE | MIL AF | 119.75 | TWR |
| | | 121.0 | APP |
| | | 123.5 | AG (CLUB FREQ) |
| | | 312.8 | TWR / APP |
| | | 259.95 | TWR / APP |

# AREA 4

## ZONES & AIRWAYS OF NW. ENGLAND & IRISH SEA

| FREQUENCY | CALL | SERVICE |
|---|---|---|
| 125.725 | VOLMET BROADCAST | SCOTTISH VOLMET |
| 131.3 | SCOTTISH INFORMATION | NORTH OF FIR |
| 127.275 | SCOTTISH INFORMATION | WEST OF FIR |
| 119.875 | SCOTTISH INFORMATION | SOUTH OF FIR |
| 134.3 | SCOTTISH MIL | RADAR & INFORMATION |
| 275.475 | SCOTTISH MIL | RADAR & INFORMATION |
| 128.425 | BORDER RADAR | UAS & TRANSIT |
| 133.875 | BORDER RADAR | UAS, MARS & TRANSIT |
| 134.7 | LONDON INFORMATION | NORTH OF FIR |
| 131.05 | LONDON INFORMATION | NORTH OF UIR |
| 128.7 | LONDON MIL (NORTH) | RADAR & INFORMATION |
| 231.625 | LONDON MIL (IRISH SEA) | RADAR & INFORMATION |
| 231.625 | LONDON MIL | UPPER AIRSPACE INFORMATION |
| 126.6 | VOLMET BROADCAST | VOLMET NORTH |
| 135.375 | VOLMET BROADCAST | VOLMET MAIN |
| 127.0 | VOLMET BROADCAST | DUBLIN VOLMET (IRISH SEA) |

NOTE:- MANCHESTER SUB CENTRE CONTROLS APPROACH TO MANCHESTER INTERNATIONAL AIRPORT AND AIRWAYS BELOW FLIGHT LEVEL 175 IN ZONE.

| | | |
|---|---|---|
| 124.2 | MANCHESTER ACC | AIRWAYS BELOW FL 155—A1, A2, A20, A47, B1, B3, B4, R3, R101, W2D, B53. |
| 125.1 | MANCHESTER ACC | AIRWAYS BELOW FL 155—A25, B1, B3, R3, W911D, B53. |
| 133.05 | MANCHESTER ACC | AIRWAYS BELOW FL 155—A25, B1, B3, W2D, W927D. |
| 126.65 | MANCHESTER ACC | AIRWAYS BELOW FL 155—A1, A2, A20, A47, B1, B4, R101, W2D, |
| 121.025 | LONDON CONTROL | AIRWAYS—A2, A20, A30, A47, B3, B4, R41, UA2, UB3, UB4, UA47, UB317, UR41. |
| 126.875 | LONDON CONTROL | AIRWAYS—A1, A25, B4, R3, R101, W927D, UAI, UA2, UA25, UB4, UB1, UR4. |
| 128.05 | LONDON CONTROL | AIRWAYS—A25, B3, B1, B53, B39. R3, W2D, W927D, UA34, UB1, UB3, UB39. |
| 129.1 | LONDON CONTROL | AIRWAYS—A1, A25, B3, B1, R3, R101, W2D, W927D, UA1, UA2, UA25, UA34, UA251. |
| 132.9 | BORDER RADAR | AIRWAYS—W9, 11D, |

# AREA 4

## ZONES & AIRWAYS OF NW. ENGLAND & IRISH SEA

| FREQUENCY | CALL | SERVICE |
|---|---|---|
| 131.05 | LONDON CONTROL | AIRWAYS—A1, A2, A20, A47, B1, B4, R101, W2D, UA1, UA2, UA25, UA251, UB1, UB4, UR4. |
| 134.25 | LONDON CONTROL | AIRWAYS—B1, B5, UA37, UB1, UB5,UB105, UL7, UL74, UR4, |
| 134.425 | LONDON CONTROL | AIRWAYS—A1, A2, A25, B1, B4, R3, R101, W2D, W927D, UAI, UA2, UA25, UB1, UB4, UR3, UR4, |
| 136.2 | LONDON CONTROL | AIRWAYS—A1, A2, A20, A47, B1, R101, W2D, UA1, UA2, UB4, |

NOTE:- MANCHESTER SUB CENTRE CONTROLS APPROACH TO MANCHESTER INTERNATIONAL AIRPORT AND AIRWAYS BELOW FLIGHT LEVEL 175 IN ZONE.

# AREA 4

## AIRFIELDS OF WEST MIDLANDS & N. WALES

| STATION | TYPE | FREQUENCY | SERVICE / REMARKS / CALL |
|---|---|---|---|
| **LIVERPOOL** | CIV AP | 118.1 | TWR |
| | | 119.85 | APP / RAD |
| | | 118.45 | RAD |
| **HAYDOCK PARK** | PRI AF | 119.4 | MANCHESTER APP |
| | | 119.85 | LIVERPOOL APP |
| **MANCHESTER (BARTON)** | CIV AF | 122.7 | AG RADIO |

NOTE:- MANCHESTER SUB CENTRE CONTROLS APPROACH TO MANCHESTER INTERNATIONAL AIRPORT AND AIRWAYS BELOW FLIGHT LEVEL 175 IN ZONE. SEE SECTION ON ZONES & AIRWAYS ABOVE.

| STATION | TYPE | FREQUENCY | SERVICE / REMARKS / CALL |
|---|---|---|---|
| **MANCHESTER AIRPORT** | CIV AP | 121.85 | INITIAL CALL IN OP HRS |
| | | 118.625 | TWR |
| | | 121.7 | GRND |
| | | 128.175 | ATIS |
| | | 119.4 | APP / RAD |
| | | 121.35 | APP RAD |
| | | 121.6 | FIRE |
| | | 130.65 | EXECUTIVE HANDLING |

# AREA 4

## AIRFIELDS OF WEST MIDLANDS & N. WALES

| STATION | TYPE | FREQUENCY | SERVICE / REMARKS / CALL |
|---|---|---|---|
| **WOODFORD** | PRI AF | 126.925 | TWR / APP |
| | | 130.75 | APP |
| | | 130.05 | RAD |
| | | *269.125* | *TWR / RAD* |
| | | *358.575* | *APP / RAD* |
| **ASHCROFT** | PRI AF | 122.525 | AG RADIO |
| **CHESTER** | CIV AF | 124.95 | TWR |
| **(HAWARDEN)** | | 123.35 | APP |
| | | 129.85 | RAD |
| | | *336.325* | *TWR* |
| **CHETWYND** | MIL AF | *309.55* | *TWR (TERNHILL)* |
| | | *276.075* | *APP (TERNHILL)* |
| **MONA** | MIL AF | 122.0 | AG RADIO / AFIS |
| | | 134.35 | VALLEY APP / MATZ |
| | | *358.75* | *TWR* |
| | | *372.325* | *VALLEY APP* |
| | | *379.7* | *APP* |
| **VALLEY** | MIL AF | 122.1 | TWR / APP / GRND |
| | | 134.35 | APP / MATZ / LARS |
| | | 123.3 | DIRECTOR / PAR RAD |
| | | *340.175* | *TWR* |
| | | *257.8* | *TWR* |
| | | *386.9* | *GRND* |
| | | *372.325* | *APP* |
| | | *362.3* | *APP* |
| | | *337.725* | *DIR / RAD* |
| | | *344.0* | *RAD* |
| | | *268.775* | *RAD / SRE* |
| | | *358.675* | *PAR RADAR* |
| | | *385.4* | *PAR RADAR* |
| | | *282.8* | *SAR* |
| **CAERNARFON** | CIV AF | 122.25 | AG RADIO |
| | | 134.35 | VALLEY APP |
| | | 122.5 | LLANBEDR APP |
| **LLANBEDR** | MIL AF | 122.5 | TWR / APP / PAR RAD |
| | | *380.175* | *TWR* |
| | | *386.675* | *APP / PAR RADAR* |
| **WELSHPOOL** | PRI AF | 124.15 | SHAWBURY APP |
| **(OAKS FARM)** | | | |

# AREA 4

## AIRFIELDS OF WEST MIDLANDS & N. WALES

| STATION | TYPE | FREQUENCY | SERVICE / REMARKS / CALL |
|---|---|---|---|
| **WELSHPOOL** (TRELIG) | PRI AF | 123.25 | AG RADIO |
| **TATENHILL** | PRI AF | 122.2 | AG RADIO |
| **WHITCHURCH** | PRI AF | 130.4 | AG RADIO |
| **WHITCHURCH** (TISTOCK) | PRI AF | 129.9 | AG RADIO |
| **MOAT HALL** | PRI AF | 122.2 | AG (TATENHILL RADIO) |
| **SHAWBURY** | MIL AF | 122.1 | TWR |
| | | 124.15 | APP / RAD / MATZ / LARS |
| | | 123.3 | PAR RADAR |
| | | *269.1* | *TWR* |
| | | *257.8* | *TWR* |
| | | *337.9* | *GRND* |
| | | *276.075* | *APP* |
| | | *362.3* | *APP* |
| | | *254.2* | *LARS / MATZ* |
| | | *386.875* | *RADAR* |
| | | *344.0* | *RADAR* |
| | | *356.975* | *PAR RADAR* |
| | | *385.4* | *PAR RADAR* |
| **TERNHILL** | MIL AF | 124.15 | TWR / APP / MATZ |
| | | 122.1 | APP |
| | | 124.15 | SHAWBURY APP / MATZ |
| | | *338.825* | *TWR* |
| | | *309.55* | *CHETWYND TRAFFIC* |
| | | *276.825* | *APP* |
| | | *365.075* | *APP* |
| | | *362.3* | *APP* |
| **SLEAP** | CIV AF | 122.45 | AG RADIO |
| | | 124.15 | SHAWBURY APP |
| **LEDBURY** (VELCOURT) | PRI AF | 125.65 | GLOUCESTER APP |
| **HALFPENNY GREEN** | CIV AF | 123.0 | AG RADIO / AFIS |
| | | 121.95 | GRND |
| **SHOBDEN** | CIV AF | 123.5 | AG RADIO |
| **COSFORD** | MIL AF | 122.1 | TWR |
| | | *357.125* | *TWR* |
| | | *276.125* | *APP* |
| | | *362.3* | *APP* |

# AREA 5

## ZONES & AIRWAYS OF THE WEST MIDLANDS

| FREQUENCY | CALL | SERVICE |
|---|---|---|
| 135.15 | LONDON MIL (SOUTH) | RADAR & INFORMATION. |
| 128.7 | LONDON MIL (NORTH) | RADAR & INFORMATION |
| 135.15 | LONDON MIL (SOUTH) | RADAR & INFORMATION |
| 275.475 | LONDON MIL | RADAR & INFORMATION |
| 134.7 | LONDON INFORMATION | NORTHERN FIR |
| 124.75 | LONDON INFORMATION | SOUTH WESTERN FIR |
| 134.7 | LONDON INFORMATION | NORTH OF FIR |
| 131.05 | LONDON INFORMATION | NORTH OF UIR |
| 132.6 | LONDON INFORMATION | SOUTH OF UIR |
| 135.15 | LONDON MIL | RADAR & INFORMATION |
| 275.475 | LONDON MIL | RADAR & INFORMATION |
| 127.45 | LONDON MIL (NORTH) | UPPER AIRSPACE INFORMATION |
| 231.625 | LONDON MIL (IRISH SEA) | UPPER AIRSPACE INFORMATION |
| 120.5 | BIRMINGHAM RADAR | |
| 134.3 | BRIZE RADR | |
| 257.1 | BRIZE RADAR | |
| 126.6 | VOLMET BROADCAST | VOLMET NORTH |
| 135.375 | VOLMET BROADCAST | VOLMET MAIN |
| 128.6 | VOLMET BROADCAST | VOLMET SOUTH |
| 127.0 | VOLMET BROADCAST | VOLMET DUBLIN |
| 121.025 | LONDON CONTROL | AIRWAYS—A2, A20, A30, A47, B3, B4, R41, UA2, UB3, UB4, UA47, UB317, UR41, |
| 126.875 | LONDON CONTROL | AIRWAYS—A1, A25, B4, R3, R101, W927D,UAI, UA2, UA25, UB4, UB1. |
| 127.1 | LONDON CONTROL | AIRWAYS—A2, A20, A47, B3, B4, B317,R41, UB3, UA47, UB4, UB317, |
| 127.425 | LONDON CONTROL | AIRWAYS—UA1, UA2, UB3, UB4, UB29, UB39, UG1, UG45, UG106, UL1, UR1, UR8, UR12, UR29, UR37, UR41, UR84, UR123, UA20, UA27, UA34, UA37, UA47, U8A30, UB11, UB39, UB71, UB295, UG39, UG45 |
| 127.875 | LONDON CONTROL | AIRWAYS—A2, A20, B3, B4, B317, R41, UA2, UB4, UB317, |
| 128.05 | LONDON CONTROL | AIRWAYS—A25, B3, B1, B53, B39. R3, W2D, W927D, UA34, UB1, UB3, UB39, |
| 129.1 | LONDON CONTROL | AIRWAYS—A1, A25, B3, B1, R3, R101, W2D, W927D, UA1, UA2, UA25, UA34, UA251. |
| 129.2 | LONDON CONTROL | AIRWAYS—B321, UB3. |

| 131.05 | LONDON CONTROL | AIRWAYS—A1, A2, A20, A47, B1, B4, R101, W2D, UA1, UA2, UA25, UA251, UB1, UB4, UR4, |
| 131.125 | LONDON CONTROL | AIRWAYS—A1, A20, A47, B3, B4, B317, B321, R41, UA1, UA2, UA34, UB3, UA 47, UB4, UB71, UB317, UR41, |
| 131.2 | LONDON CONTROL | AIRWAYS—G1, B10, R14, R41, UA29, UP2, UR41, UR14, UB10, UN546. |
| 132.8 | LONDON CONTROL | AIRWAYS—B321, G1, R41, UA251, UB29, UB39, UB295, UG1, UP2, UL1 UR41. |
| 132.9 | BORDER RADAR | AIRWAYS—W911D, |
| 133.7 | LONDON CONTROL | AIRWAYS—A1, A2, A20, A47, B3, B4, R41, B317, B321, UA1, UA2, UA34, UA47, UB3, UB4, UB71, UB317, UR41, |
| 134.425 | LONDON CONTROL | AIRWAYS—A1, A2, A25, B1, B4, R3, R101, W2D, W927D, UAI, UA2, UA25, UB1, UB4, UR3, UR4, |
| 134.75 | LONDON CONTROL | AIRWAYS—UA1, UA2, UA.34, UA30, UA47, UB29, UB39, UB295, UG1, UG39, UR1, UR12, UR123, UR4, UR8, UR37, |
| 134.9 | LONDON CONTROL | AIRWAYS—B3, B4, B317, R8, UB3, UB71, UG1, UG106, UL1, UR37, |
| 136.2 | LONDON CONTROL | AIRWAYS—A1, A2, A20, A47, B1, R101, W2D, UA1, UA2, UB4, |

# AREA 5

## AIRFIELDS OF THE MIDLANDS & THAMES VALLEY

| STATION | TYPE | FREQUENCY | SERVICE / REMARKS / CALL |
|---|---|---|---|
| **BIRMINGHAM** | CIV AP | 118.3 | TWR |
| | | 121.8 | GRND |
| | | 126.275 | ATIS |
| | | 131.325 | ATC |
| | | 118.05 | APP / RAD |
| | | 21.6 | FIRE |
| | | 131.85 | EXECUTIVE OPS |
| **COVENTRY** | CIV AP | 124.8 | TWR / GRND |
| | | 121.7 | GRND |
| | | 119.25 | TWR / APP / RAD |
| | | 122.0 | RAD / SRE |
| **WELLSBOURNE MOUNTFORD** | CIV AF | 124.025 | AG RADIO |

# AREA 5

## AIRFIELDS OF THE MIDLANDS & THAMES VALLEY

| STATION | TYPE | FREQUENCY | SERVICE / REMARKS / CALL |
|---|---|---|---|
| **NORTHAMPTON (SYWELL)** | CIV AF | 122.7 | AG RADIO / AFIS |
| **WESTON ON THE GREEN** | MIL AF | 133.65 | TWR CALL RAF |
| | | 134.3 | TWR CALL RAF |
| | | *255.1* | *BRIZE RADAR* |
| **CROUGHTON** | MIL USAF | 17.975 KHz | AG RADIO (SSB) |
| | | 15.015 KHz | AG RADIO (SSB) |
| | | 13.201 KHz | AG RADIO (SSB) |
| | | 11.176 KHz | AG RADIO (SSB) |
| | | 8.967 KHz | AG RADIO (SSB) |
| | | 6.750 KHz | AG RADIO (SSB) |
| | | 4.725 KHz | AG RADIO (SSB) |
| | | *343.6* | *AG RADIO* |
| **HINTON-IN-THE-HEDGES** | PRI AF | 119.45 | AIR TO AIR |
| **ENSTONE** | CIV AF | 129.875 | AG RADIO |
| **TURWESTON** | PRI AF | 122.175 | AG RADIO |
| **SILVERSTONE** | PRI AF | 121.075 | TWR / AG |
| **CHALGROVE** | PRI AF | 125.4 | AG RADIO |
| **OXFORD (KIDLINGTON)** | CIV AF | 118.875 | TWR / AG RADIO / AFIS |
| | | 121.75 | GRND |
| | | 121.75 | ATIS |
| | | 125.325 | APP |
| | | 128.325 | APP |
| | | 130.3 | APP |
| | | 134.3 | BRIZE RADAR |
| | | 132.65 | OXFORD COLLEGE |
| **REDLANDS** | PRI AF | 129.825 | AG RADIO |
| **ABINGDON (SEE BENSON)** | MIL AF | 134.3 | BRIZE RADAR |
| **BENSON** | MIL AF | 130.25 | TWR |
| | | 122.1 | TWR / APP / DIR |
| | | 120.9 | APP / RAD / MATZ |
| | | 127.15 | APP |
| | | 123.775 | DIRECTOR / SRE |
| | | 134.3 | BRIZE RADAR |
| | | *279.35* | *TWR* |

# AREA 5

## AIRFIELDS OF THE MIDLANDS & THAMES VALLEY

| STATION | TYPE | FREQUENCY | SERVICE / REMARKS / CALL |
|---|---|---|---|
| **BENSON (Continued)** | | 340.325 | GRND |
| | | 268/825 | APP |
| | | 344.0 | APP / DIR |
| | | 315.75 | DIR /SRE |
| | | 358.8 | BENSON ZONE |
| | | 362.3 | BENSON ZONE |
| | | 361.875 | PAR RADAR |
| | | 275.475 | RADAR (LONDON MIL) |
| | | 257.1 | BRIZE RADAR |

# AMENDMENTS

| STATION | TYPE | FREQUENCY | SERVICE / REMARKS / CALL |
|---|---|---|---|

# AREA 5A

## ZONES & AIRWAYS OF SOUTH MIDLANDS & SOUTH WALES

| FREQUENCY | CALL | SERVICE |
|---|---|---|
| 120.5 | BIRMINGHAM RADAR | |
| 135.15 | LONDON MIL (SOUTH) | RADAR & INFORMATION. |
| 128.7 | LONDON MIL (NORTH) | RADAR & INFORMATION |
| 135.15 | LONDON MIL (SOUTH) | RADAR & INFORMATION |
| 275.475 | LONDON MIL | RADAR & INFORMATION |
| 134.7 | LONDON INFORMATION | NORTHERN FIR |
| 124.75 | LONDON INFORMATION | SOUTH WESTERN FIR |
| 132.6 | LONDON INFORMATION | UIR |
| 135.15 | LONDON MIL | RADAR & INFORMATION |
| 275.475 | LONDON MIL | RADAR & INFORMATION |
| 127.45 | LONDON MIL (NORTH) | UPPER AIRSPACE INFORMATION |
| 231.625 | LONDON MIL (IRISH SEA) | UPPER AIRSPACE INFORMATION |
| 125.85 | CARDIFF RADAR | |
| 134.3 | BRIZE RADAR | |
| 257.1 | BRIZE RADAR | |
| 126.6 | VOLMET BROADCAST | VOLMET NORTH |
| 135.375 | VOLMET BROADCAST | VOLMET MAIN |
| 128.6 | VOLMET BROADCAST | VOLMET SOUTH |
| 127.0 | VOLMET BROADCAST | VOLMET DUBLIN |
| 118.475 | LONDON CONTROL | AIRWAYS—R1, R12, R123, R126, UA37, UB29, UB317, UR1, UR12, UR123, UR126, B29. |
| 127.875 | LONDON CONTROL | AIRWAYS—A2, A20, B3, B4, B317, R41, UA2, UB4, UB317, |
| 127.95 | LONDON CONTROL | AIRWAYS—B317, B29, R1, R12, R123, R126, UA37, UB29, UB317, UG39, UR1, UR12, UR123, UR126, |
| 128.05 | LONDON CONTROL | AIRWAYS—A25, B3, B1, B53, B39. R3, W2D, W927D, UA34, UB1, UB3, UB39. |
| 128.425 | LONDON CONTROL | AIRWAYS—A2, A20, B3, B4, B317, R8, UA2, UB3, UA20, UA30, UB4, UG1, UG106, UL1, UR37, |
| 129.6 | LONDON CONTROL | AIRWAYS—B317, B29, R1, R12, R123, R126, UA37, UB317, UG39, UR1, UR12, UR123, UR126, |
| 131.05 | LONDON CONTROL | AIRWAYS—A1, A2, A20, A47, B1, B4, R101, W2D, UA1, UA2, UA25, UA251, UB1, UB4, UR4, |
| 131.125 | LONDON CONTROL | AIRWAYS—A1, A20, A47, B3, B4, B317, B321, R41, UA1, UA2, UA34, UB3, UA 47, UB4, UB71, UB317, UR41. |

# AREA 5A

## ZONES & AIRWAYS OF SOUTH MIDLANDS & SOUTH WALES

| FREQUENCY | CALL | SERVICE |
|---|---|---|
| 131.2 | LONDON CONTROL | AIRWAYS—G1, B10, R14, R41, UA29, UP2, UR41, UR14, UB10, UN546, |
| 131.325 | BIRMINGHAM ZONE | |
| 132.6 | LONDON CONTROL | AIRWAYS—R8, R37, UA25, UL722, UL1, UN862, UN863, UN865, UR72, UR168, UR14, UR116, UR40, UR8, UR37, UT7. |
| 132.8 | LONDON CONTROL | AIRWAYS—B321, G1, R41, UA251, UB29, UB39, UB295, UG1, UP2, UL1, UR41. |
| 133.45 | LONDON CONTROL | AIRWAYS—R1, R12, R123, UB317, UR1 UR12, UR123. |
| 133.525 | LONDON CONTROL | AIRWAYS—B1, B5, R1, R12, R123,UB1, UA37, UB5, UR1, UR4, UR12, UR123, UR126, UB29, UB105, UB317, UG39. |
| 133.6 | LONDON CONTROL | AIRWAYS—B10, UB10, UB39, UB40, B321, UA25, UA29, UB29, UB295, UP2. |
| 133.7 | LONDON CONTROL | AIRWAYS—A1, A2, A20, A47, B3, B4, B317, B321, UA1, UA2, UA34, UA47, UB3, UB4, UB71, UB317, UR41, |
| 134.75 | LONDON CONTROL | AIRWAYS—UA1, UA2, UA.34, UA30, UA47, UB29, UB39, UB295, UG1, UG39, UR1, UR12, UR123, UR4, UR8, UR37. |
| 134.9 | LONDON CONTROL | AIRWAYS—B3, B4, B317, R8, UB3, UB71, UG1, UG106, UL1, UR37. |
| 135.05 | LONDON CONTROL | AIRWAYS—A47, R37, UA47, UB4, UN862, UN863, UN865. |
| 135.325 | LONDON CONTROL | AIRWAYS—A1, A34, A47, A56, B11, R1, R803, UA1, UA34, UB11, UR1, UR12, UR123, R84, UR41, UR8, UR24, UR25, UR37, UR84. |
| 136.275 | LONDON CONTROL | AIRWAYS—B4, B5, R1, R12, R123, UB1, UB5, UB29, UB29, UB317, UB105, UR1. UR12, UR123, UR4, UR126. |
| 136.55 | LONDON CONTROL | AIRWAYS—B317, B29, R1, R12, R123, UA37, UB29, UB317, UR1, UR12, UR123, UR126. |

# AREA 5A

## AIRFIELDS OF THE UPPER THAMES VALLEY & SOUTH WALES

| STATION | TYPE | FREQUENCY | SERVICE / REMARKS / CALL |
|---|---|---|---|
| **NEWBURY** | PRI AF | 134.3 | BRIZE RADAR |
| **RACECOURSE** | | 126.7 | BOSCOMBE APP |
| **BRIZE NORTON** | MIL AF | 126.5 | TWR / GRND |
| | | 133.75 | DIR / APP |
| | | 130.075 | OPS |
| | | 119.0 | DIR / SRE / MATZ / LARS |
| | | 134.3 | BRIZE RADAR / LARS |
| | | 123.3 | PAR / SRE |
| | | *381.2* | *TWR* |
| | | *257.8* | *TWR* |
| | | *370.3* | *GRND* |
| | | *357.475* | *OPS* |
| | | *342.45* | *APP* |
| | | *362.3* | *APP* |
| | | *257.1* | *BRIZE RAD / LARS/MARS* |
| | | *356.975* | *DIR / APP / RAD* |
| | | *344.0* | *DIR / APP / RAD* |
| | | *338.65* | *PAR RAD* |
| | | *385.4* | *PAR RAD* |
| **WROUGHTON** | MIL AF | 133.65 | TWR |
| | | 123.225 | AG RADIO |
| | | *315.1* | *TWR* |
| **DRAYCOTT** | PRI AF | 118.425 | LYNEHAM APP |
| **LYNEHAM** | MIL AF | 122.1 | TWR / GRND |
| | | 118.425 | TWR / GRND / APP |
| | | 123.4 | DIRECTOR / APP / RAD |
| | | 134.3 | BRIZE RADAR |
| | | 123.3 | PAR RADAR |
| | | *386.825* | *TWR* |
| | | *340.175* | *GRND* |
| | | *381.0* | *ATIS* |
| | | *359.5* | *APP* |
| | | *362.3* | *APP* |
| | | *300.475* | *DIR* |
| | | *344.00* | *DIR* |
| | | *375.2* | *PAR RADAR* |
| | | *385.4* | *PAR RADAR* |
| **OAKSEY PARK** | PRI AF | 122.777 | AG RADIO |
| | | 123.4 | LYNHAM APP |

# AREA 5A

## AIRFIELDS OF THE UPPER THAMES VALLEY & SOUTH WALES

| STATION | TYPE | FREQUENCY | SERVICE / REMARKS / CALL |
|---|---|---|---|
| **FAIRFORD** | MIL USAF | 142.225 | TWR |
| | | 122.1 | TWR / APP /BRIZE RADAR |
| | | 119.0 | BRIZE DIR / MATZ |
| | | 134.3 | MATZ /BRIZE RADAR |
| | | *337.575* | *TWR* |
| | | *257.8* | *TWR* |
| | | *259.975* | *GRND* |
| | | *379.475* | *DISPATCHER* |
| | | *307.8* | *COMMAND POST* |
| | | *371.2* | *COMMAND POST* |
| | | *358.6* | *FAIRFORD METRO* |
| | | *376.625* | *BRIZE RADAR / MATZ* |
| | | *275.1* | *BRIZE RADAR* |
| **BADMINTON** | PRI AF | 123.175 | AG RADIO |
| | | 123.4 | LYNEHAM APP |
| | | 122.725 | FILTON APP |
| **GLOUCESTERSHIRE** | CIV AP | 122.9 | TWR |
| | | 127.475 | ATIS |
| | | 125.65 | APP |
| | | 120.975 | RAD |
| | | 121.6 | FIRE |
| **FILTON (BRISTOL)** | PRI AF | 132.35 | TWR |
| | | 127.275 | APP |
| | | 122.725 | APP / RAD / LARS |
| | | 127.975 | RAD |
| | | 342.025 | TWR |
| | | 256.125 | APP / RAD / LARS |
| | | 336.475 | DIR |

# AREA 5A

## AIRFIELDS OF THE SEVERN VALLEY & SOUTH WALES

| STATION | TYPE | FREQUENCY | SERVICE / REMARKS / CALL |
|---|---|---|---|
| **PORTISHEAD RADIO** | (HF STN) | 131.635 | AG RADIO |
| | | 25109 KHz | AG RADIO (SSB) |
| | | 20065 KHz | AG RADIO (SSB) |
| | | 19510 KHz | AG RADIO (SSB) |
| | | 18210 KHz | AG RADIO (SSB) |
| | | 17335 KHz | AG RADIO (SSB) |
| | | 16273 KHz | AG RADIO (SSB) |
| | | 15964 KHz | AG RADIO (SSB) |
| | | 14890 KHz | AG RADIO (SSB) |
| | | 12133 KHz | AG RADIO (SSB) |
| | | 11306 KHz | AG RADIO (SSB) |
| | | IO291 KHz | AG RADIO (SSB) |
| | | 8960 KHz | AG RADIO (SSB) |
| | | 8170 KHz | AG RADIO (SSB) |
| | | 6634 KHz | AG RADIO (SSB) |
| | | 5610 KHz | AG RADIO (SSB) |
| | | 4087 KHz | AG RADIO (SSB) |
| **BRISTOL AIRPORT** | CIV AP | 133.85 | TWR |
| | | 126.025 | ATIS |
| | | 120.6 | APP |
| | | 132.4 | LARS |
| | | 124.35 | RAD |
| **WESTBURY-SUB-MENDIP** | PRI AF | 132.4 | BRISTOL APP |
| | | 127.35 | YEOVILTON APP |
| **WESTON-SUPER-MARE** | PRI AF | 122.5 | TWR |
| | | 129.25 | APP |
| *CARDIFF* | CIV AP | 125.0 | TWR |
| | | 119.475 | ATIS |
| | | 125.85 | APP / RAD / LARS |
| | | 124.1 | PAR RADAR |
| | | 277.225 | APP / RAD |
| **ST ATHAN** | MIL AF | 122.1 | TWR / APP |
| | | 119.475 | ATIS CARDIFF INFO |
| | | 125.85 | CARDIFF APP |
| | | 123.3 | RAD / DIRECTOR |
| | | *336.525* | *TWR* |
| | | *257.8* | *TWR* |
| | | *227.225* | *CARDIFF APP* |
| | | *357.175* | *APP* |
| | | *362.3* | *APP* |

# AREA 5A

## AIRFIELDS OF THE SEVERN VALLEY & SOUTH WALES

| STATION | TYPE | FREQUENCY | SERVICE / REMARKS / CALL |
|---------|------|-----------|--------------------------|
| ST ATHAN (continued) | | 380.125 | DIR |
| | | 340.1 | DIR / PAR |
| TREMORFA HELIPORT | CIV PAD | 129.9 | AG RADIO |
| | | 125.85 | CARDIFF APP |
| SWANSEA | CIV AF | 119.7 | TWR / APP |
| | | 120.75 | RAD |
| BRAWDY | MIL AF | 122.4 | AG / BRAWDY RESCUE |
| | | 123.1 | SAR |
| HAVERFORD WEST | CIV AF | 122.2 | AG RADIO |
| | | 124.4 | BRAWDY RESCUE |
| MANORBIER | MIL RANGE | 336.225 | AG RADIO |
| | | 360.777 | AG RADIO |
| ABERPORTH | MIL AF | 122.15 | AFIS |
| | | 259.0 | TWR |

# SOME OFFSHORE OIL & GAS FIELD RELATED FREQUENCIES

| FREQUENCY | FIELD | OPERATING COMPANY |
|-----------|-------|-------------------|
| 122.05 | MURCHISON | CONOCO |
| 122.05 | THISTLE | BRITOIL |
| 122.05 | EIDER | SHELL / ESSO |
| 122.25 | BRENT | SHELL / ESSO |
| 122.375 395 | MAGNUS | BP |
| 122.8 | HEATHER | UNIONOIL |
| 129.65 | STATFJORD | MOBIL / STATOIL |
| 129.95 | TERN | SHELL / ESSO |
| 129.95 | DUNLIN | SHELL / ESSO |
| 129.95 | N. CORMORANT | SHELL / ESSO |
| 130.8 | NW HUTTON | AMOCO |
| 130.2 | NINIAN | CHEVRON |
| 122.35 | ALWYN | OTAL |
| 122.35 | DUNBAR | TOTAL |
| 122.525 | EMERALD | SOVEREIGN |
| 129.75 | FRIGG | TOTAL / ELF |
| 122.75 | BERYL | MOBIL |

# SOME OFFSHORE OIL & GAS FIELD RELATED FREQUENCIES

| FREQUENCY | FIELD | OPERATING COMPANY |
|---|---|---|
| 130.725 | FRIGG/STFS PIP | TOTAL / ELF |
| 123.65 | BRAE | MARATHON |
| 122.45 | CLAYMORE | ELF/ENTERPRISE CALEDONIA |
| 122.45 | PIPER | ELF ENTERPRISE CALEDONIA |
| 122.45 | TARTAN | TEXACO |
| 123.55 | BALMORAL | SUN OIL |
| 122.175 | IVANHOE | ANERADA HESS |
| 123.65 | BEATRICE | BRITOIL |
| 123.55 | MAUREEN | PHILLIPS |
| 122.0 | BUCHAN | BP |
| 122.0 | FORTES | BP |
| 129.7 | MONTROSE | AMOCO |
| 129.7 | ARBROATH | AMOCO |
| 130.55 | COD | PHILLIPS |
| 130.55 | ABUSKJELL | PHILLIPS |
| 130.55 | TOR | PHILLIPS |
| 130.55 | EKOFISK | PHILLIPS |
| 129.7 | GANNET | SHELL / ESSO |
| 122.02 | FULMAR | SHELL / ESSO |
| 122.02 | AUK | SHELL / ESSO |
| 122.525 | CLYDE | BRITOIL |
| 130.55 | EDDA | PHILLIPS |
| 130.55 | ELDFISK | PHILLIPS |
| 130.55 | VALHALL | AMOCO |
| 122.95 | EKOFISK / TEES-SIDE | PHILLIPS |
| 123.45 | TYRA | MAERSK |
| 123.45 | GORM | MAERSK |
| 123.45 | DAN | MAERSK |
| 123.45 | SKJOLD | MAERSK |
| 129.9 | EMDEN | PHILLIPS |
| 122.325 | ESMOND | HAMILTON |
| 122.325 | GORDON | HAMILTON |
| 123.025 | RAVENSPURN | HAMILTON |
| 129.875 | ROUGH | BRITISH GAS |
| 129.875 | WEST SOLE | BP |
| 129.875 | AMETHYST | BP |
| 122.375 | MORECAMBE | BRITISH GAS |
| 122.95 | PETROLAND | PETROLAND |
| 122.625 }<br>120.075 } | VIKING | CONOCO |
| 122.95 | NAM | NAM |
| 122.95 | PLACID | PLACID |

# SOME OFFSHORE OIL & GAS FIELD RELATED FREQUENCIES

| FREQUENCY | FIELD | OPERATING COMPANY |
|---|---|---|
| 122.95 | NOORDWINNING | WINTERSHALL |
| 123.45 | CLIPPER | SHELL / ESSO |
| 123.625 | INDEFATIGABLE | SHELL / ESSO |
| 122.95 | NOORDWINNING / ZANDDLJK. | NAM |
| 122.875 | HEWETT | PHILLIPS |
| 123.225 | THAMES | ARCO |
| 123.625 | LEMAN | SHELL / ESSO |
| 123.45 | CAMELOT | MOBIL |
| 123.45 | EAST KINSALE | MARATHON |
| 123.45 | WEST KINSALE | MARATHON |

It should be noted that all above VHF frequencies are for helicopters and military aircraft on surveillance operations. As much of the activity is many miles offshore reception on these channels may not be possible on the mainland.

# AMENDMENTS

| STATION | TYPE | FREQUENCY | SERVICE / REMARKS / CALL |
|---|---|---|---|

# IMPORTANT NOTE

THE AREAS USED IN THIS GUIDE ARE FOR CONVENIENCE OF DISPLAYING INFORMATION AND SHOULD NOT BE REGARDED AS ACCURATE AND NEVER USED FOR NAVIGATION.

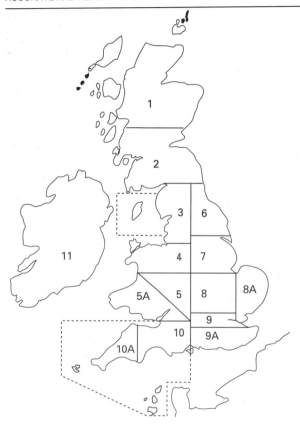

# AREA 6

## ZONES & AIRWAYS OF THE NORTH EAST OF ENGLAND

| FREQUENCY | CALL | SERVICE |
|---|---|---|
| 124.5 | | NORTHERN RADAR ADVISORY |
| 121.5 | | EMERGENCY THROUGH ATCC |
| 243.0 | | EMERGENCY THROUGH ATCC |
| 126.25 | SCOTTISH CONTROL | AIRWAYS—A1, A25 |
| 123.357 | SCOTTISH CONTROL | AIRWAYS—A1, A2, A25, B4 |
| 126.85 | SCOTTISH CONTROL | AIRWAYS—B2, B3, B4, |
| 123.375 | SCOTTISH CONTROL | ENTERING TMA FROM SOUTH EAST |
| 126.25 | SCOTTISH CONTROL | ENTERING TMA FROM SOUTH WEST |
| 125.725 | VOLMET BROADCAST | SCOTTISH VOLMET |
| 131.3 | SCOTTISH INFORMATION | NORTH OF FIR |
| 127.275 | SCOTTISH INFORMATION | WEST OF FIR |
| 119.875 | SCOTTISH INFORMATION | SOUTH OF FIR |
| 134.3 | SCOTTISH MIL | RADAR & INFORMATION |
| 249.475 | SCOTTISH MIL | RADAR & INFORMATION |
| 128.425 | BORDER RADAR | UAS & TRANSIT |
| 133.875 | BORDER RADAR | UAS, MARS & TRANSIT |
| 134.7 | LONDON INFORMATION | NORTH OF FIR |
| 135.275 | LONDON MIL (NORTH) | RADAR & INFORMATION |
| 135.275 | LONDON MIL (NORTH) | UPPER AIRSPACE INFORMATION |
| 299.975 | LONDON MIL (NORTH) | UPPER AIRSPACE INFORMATION |
| 126.6 | VOLMET BROADCAST | VOLMET NORTH |
| 135.375 | VOLMET BROADCAST | VOLMET MAIN |
| 128.5 | SCOTTISH CONTROL | AIRWAYS |
| 126.25 | SCOTTISH CONTROL | AIRWAYS—A1, A25 |
| 123.357 | SCOTTISH CONTROL | AIRWAYS—A1, A2, A25, B4 |
| 126.85 | SCOTTISH CONTROL | AIRWAYS—B2, B3, B4, |
| 126.775 | LONDON CONTROL | AIRWAYS—B1, B5, UA37, UB1, UB5, UB105,UL7, UL74, UR4, |
| 126.875 | LONDON CONTROL | AIRWAYS—A1, A25, B4, R3, R101, W927D, UAI, UA2, UA25, UB4, UB1, |
| 128.125 | LONDON CONTROL | AIRWAYS—B1, B5, UB1, UA37, UB5, UB105, UL7, UL74, UR4, |
| 132.9 | BORDER RADAR | AIRWAYS—W911D |
| 131.05 | LONDON CONTROL | AIRWAYS—A1, A2, A20, A47, B1, B4, R101, W2D, UA1, UA2, UA25, UA251, UB1, UB4, UR4, |
| 133.525 | LONDON CONTROL | AIRWAYS—B1, B5, R1, R12, R123,UB1, UA37, UB5, UR1, UR4, UR12, UR123, UR126, UB29, UB105, UB317, UG39, |
| 134.25 | LONDON CONTROL | AIRWAYS—B1, B5, UA37, UB1, UB5, UB105, UL7, UL74, UR4, |

# AREA 6

## ZONES & AIRWAYS OF THE NORTH EAST OF ENGLAND

| FREQUENCY | CALL | SERVICE |
|---|---|---|
| 134.425 | LONDON CONTROL | AIRWAYS—A1, A2, A25, B1, B4, R3, R101, W2D, W927D, UAI, UA2, UA25, UB1, UB4, UR3, UR4, |
| 136.2 | LONDON CONTROL | AIRWAYS—A1, A2, A20, A47, B1, R101, W2D, UA1, UA2, UB4, |
| 136.275 | LONDON CONTROL | AIRWAYS—B4, B5, R1, R12, R123, UB1,UB5, UB29, UB29, UB317, UB105, UR1. UR12, UR123, UR4, UR126, |

NOTE:- MANCHESTER SUB CENTRE CONTROLS APPROACH TO MANCHESTER INTERNATIONAL AIRPORT AND AIRWAYS BELOW FLIGHT LEVEL 175 IN ZONE.

| | | |
|---|---|---|
| 124.2 | MANCHESTER ACC | AIRWAYS BELOW FL 155—A1, A2, A20,   A47, B1, B3, B4, R3, R101, W2D, B53 |
| 125.1 | MANCHESTER ACC | AIRWAYS BELOW FL 155—A25, B1, B3, R3, W911D, B53, |
| 133.05 | MANCHESTER ACC | AIRWAYS BELOW FL 155—A25, B1, B3, W2D, W927D, |
| 126.65 | MANCHESTER ACC | AIRWAYS BELOW FL 155—A1, A2, A20,   A47, B1, B4, R101, W2D, |

# AREA 6

## AIRFIELDS OF THE NORTH EASTERN COUNTIES

| STATION | TYPE | FREQUENCY | SERVICE / REMARKS / CALL |
|---|---|---|---|
| **CHARTERHALL** | PRI AF | 119.875 | SCOTTISH INFORMATION |
| **WINFIELD** | PRI AF | 123.5 | AG RADIO |
| **BOULMER** | MIL AF | 123.1 | AG RADIO |
| | | *282.8* | *SAR* |
| | | *299.1* | *AG* |
| **ESHOTT** | PRI AF | 134.7 | LONDON INFORMATION |
| | | 124.375 | NEWCASTLE APP |
| ***NEWCASTLE*** | CIV AP | 119.7 | TWR |
| ***INTERNATIONAL*** | | 114.25 | ATIS |
| | | 118.5 | APP / RAD |
| | | 124.375 | APP / LARS / RAD |
| | | 121.6 | FIRE |
| | | 122.05 | NE AVIATION |
| | | *284.6* | *APP / RAD / LARS* |

# AREA 6

## AIRFIELDS OF THE NORTH EASTERN COUNTIES

| STATION | TYPE | FREQUENCY | SERVICE / REMARKS / CALL |
|---|---|---|---|
| **FISHBURN (MORGANFIELD)** | PRI AF | 118.85 | TEES-SIDE APP |
| **TEES-SIDE** | CIV AP | 119.8 | TWR |
| | | 118.85 | APP / RAD |
| | | 128.85 | RAD |
| | | 121.6 | FIRE |
| | | 379.8 | TWR |
| | | *296.725* | *APP / RAD* |
| **LEEMING** | MIL AF | 122.1 | TWR |
| | | 132.4 | TWR |
| | | 123.3 | APP / RAD |
| | | 127.75 | APP / MATZ / LARS |
| | | *344.575* | *TWR* |
| | | *257.8* | *TWR* |
| | | *338.85* | *GRND* |
| | | *356.725* | *OPS* |
| | | *358.65* | *DIR* |
| | | *344.0* | *DIR* |
| | | *337.825* | *APP* |
| | | *362.3* | *APP* |
| | | *292.7* | *RAD / LARS* |
| | | *336.35* | *PAR RADAR* |
| | | *309.875* | *PAR RADAR* |
| | | *385.4* | *PAR RADAR* |
| **DISHFORTH** | MIL AF | 122.1 | TWR / GRND |
| | | 129.975 | AG RADIO |
| | | 129.15 | LINTON APP |
| | | 127.75 | MATZ (LEEMING) |
| | | *259.65* | *TWR* |
| | | *252.9* | *OPS* |
| **BAGBY (THIRSK)** | PRI AF | 123.25 | AG RADIO |
| | | 127.75 | LEEMING APP |
| **SUTTON BANK** | CIV AF | 130.4 | AG (GLIDER FREQ) |
| **MARSTON MOOR** | CIV AF | 122.975 | AG RADIO |
| | | 129.5 | LINTON APP |
| **POCKLINGTON** | PRI AF | 130.1 | AG RADIO |
| **FADMOOR** | PRI AF | 123.225 | AG RADIO |
| **WILLY HOWE** | PRI AG | 130.125 | AG RADIO |

# AREA 6

## AIRFIELDS OF THE NORTH EASTERN COUNTIES

| STATION | TYPE | FREQUENCY | SERVICE / REMARKS / CALL |
|---|---|---|---|
| **BRIDLINGTON** (CARNABY) | CIV AF | 123.25 | AG RADIO |
| **BERVERLEY** | PRI AF | 123.05 | AG RADIO |
| **LECONFIELD** | MIL AF | 123.05 | SAR |
| | | 244.875 | SAR |
| | | 282.8 | SAR |
| **BREIGHTON** | PRI AF | 129.8 | AG RADIO |
| **LINTON ON-OUSE** | MIL AF | 122.1 | TWR |
| | | 129.15 | AG / APP / MATZ / LARS |
| | | 123.3 | PAR RADAR |
| | | *300.425* | *TWR* |
| | | *257.8* | *TWR* |
| | | *340.025* | *GRND* |
| | | *362.675* | *APP* |
| | | *362.3* | *APP* |
| | | *292.8* | *DIR /LARS* |
| | | *344.0* | *DIR* |
| | | *358.525* | *PAR RADAR* |
| | | *259.875* | *PAR RADAR* |
| **RUFFORTH** | CIV AF | 130.4 | AF RADIO |
| | | 129.975 | AG GLIDERS ONLY |
| **TOPCLIFFE** | MIL AF | 130.825 | TWR |
| | | 122.1 | TWR / APP |
| | | 127.75 | MATZ (LEEMING) |
| | | 125.0 | APP |
| | | 123.3 | PAR RADAR |
| | | *309.725* | *TWR* |
| | | *257.8* | *TWR* |
| | | *357.375* | *APP* |
| | | *362.3* | *APP* |
| | | *344.35* | *DIR / PAR RADAR* |
| | | *385.4* | *DIR / PAR RADAR* |
| **ELVINGTON** | MIL AF | 126.5 | FENTON APP / MATZ |
| | | *352.4* | *TWR* |
| | | *371.4* | *APP* |
| **YORK** (ACASTER MALBIS) | PRI AF | 126.5 | FENTON APP |
| | | 129.15 | LINTON ZONE |
| **POCKLINGTON** | PRI AF | 130.1 | AG RADIO |

# AREA 6

## AIRFIELDS OF THE NORTH EASTERN COUNTIES

| STATION | TYPE | FREQUENCY | SERVICE / REMARKS / CALL |
|---|---|---|---|
| **CHURCH FENTON** | MIL AF | 126.5 | TWR / APP / MATZ |
| | | 122.1 | TWR / GRND |
| | | 126.5 | APP |
| | | 129.15 | LINTON DEPARTURES |
| | | 123.3 | PAR RADAR |
| | | *262.7* | *TWR* |
| | | *257.8* | *TWR* |
| | | *340.2* | *GRND* |
| | | *262.075* | *APP* |
| | | *362.3* | *APP* |
| | | *292.8* | *LINTON DEPARTURES* |
| | | 282.075 | RAD |
| | | *344.0* | *DIR* |
| | | *386.725* | *PAR RADAR* |
| | | *385.4* | *PAR RADAR* |
| **SHERBURN IN ELMET** | CIV AF | 122.6 | AG RADIO |
| | | 129.15 | LINTON APP |
| **PAULL (HULL)** | PRI AF | 123.0 | AG RADIO |
| **HULL (BURTON CONSTABLE)** | PRI AF | 122.75 | COWDEN RANGE |
| **BROUGH** | PRI AF | 130.55 | TWR / AG RADIO |
| | | *310.35* | *TWR* |
| | | *379.775* | *RAD* |
| **LEEDS / BRADFORD** | CIV AP | 120.3 | TWR |
| | | 118.025 | ATIS |
| | | 123.75 | APP / VDF |
| | | 121.05 | RAD |
| | | 121.6 | FIRE |
| **HUDDERSFIELD** | CIV AF | 122.2 | AG RADIO |

# AREA 7

## ZONES & AIRWAYS OF HUMBERSIDE & LINCS.

| FREQUENCY | CALL | SERVICE |
|---|---|---|
| 128.425 | BORDER RADAR | AS & TRANSIT |
| 133.875 | BORDER RADAR | UAS, MARS & TRANSIT |
| 134.7 | LONDON INFORMATION | NORTH OF FIR |
| 124.6 | LONDON INFORMATION | SOUTH OF FIR |
| I31.05 | LONDON INFORMATION | NORTH OF UIR |
| 132.6 | LONDON INFORMATION | SOUTH OF UIR |
| 135.275 | LONDON MIL (NORTH) | RADAR & INFORMATION |
| 135.275 | LONDON MIL (NORTH) | UPPER AIRSPACE INFORMATION |
| 299.975 | LONDON MIL (NORTH) | UPPER AIRSPACE INFORMATION |
| 126.6 | VOLMET BROADCAST | VOLMET NORTH |
| 135.375 | VOLMET BROADCAST | VOLMET MAIN |
| 125.275 | ANGLIA RADAR | RADAR & INFORMATION |
| 128.925 | ANGLIA RADAR | RADAR & INFORMATION |
| 126.775 | LONDON CONTROL | AIRWAYS—B1, B5, UA37, UB1, UB5, UB105,UL7, UL74, UR4, |
| 126.875 | LONDON CONTROL | AIRWAYS—A1, A25, B4, R3, R101, W927D, UAI, UA2, UA25, UB4, UB1. |
| 128.125 | LONDON CONTROL | AIRWAYS—B1, B5, UB1, UA37, UB5, UB105, UL7, UL74, UR4, |
| 131.05 | LONDON CONTROL | AIRWAYS—A1, A2, A20, A47, B1, B4, R101, W2D, UA1, UA2, UA25, UA251, UB1, UB4, UR4. |
| 133.525 | LONDON CONTROL | AIRWAYS—B1, B5, R1, R12, R123,UB1, UA37, UB5, UR1, UR4, UR12, UR123, UR126, UB29, UB105, UB317, UG39, |
| 134.25 | LONDON CONTROL | AIRWAYS—B1, B5, UA37, UB1, UB5, UB105, UL7, UL74, UR4, |
| 134.425 | LONDON CONTROL | AIRWAYS—A1, A2, A25, B1, B4, R3, R101, W2D, W927D, UAI, UA2, UA25, UB1, UB4, UR3, UR4. |
| 136.2 | LONDON CONTROL | AIRWAYS—A1, A2, A20, A47, B1, R101, W2D, UA1, UA2, UB4. |
| 136.275 | LONDON CONTROL | AIRWAYS—B4, B5, R1, R12, R123, UB1, UB5, UB29, UB29, UB317, B105, UR1. UR12, UR123, UR4, UR126, |

# AREA 7

## AIRFIELDS OF HUMBERSIDE, E. MIDLANDS & LINCS.

| STATION | TYPE | FREQUENCY | SERVICE / REMARKS / CALL |
|---|---|---|---|
| **HUMBERSIDE INTL AIRPORT** | CIV AP | 118.55 | TWR |
| | | 124.675 | TWR / APP |
| | | 124.125 | ATIS |
| | | 123.15 | RAD |
| **GRIMSBY (CUXWOLD)** | PRI AF | 122.35 | AG RADIO |
| **DONNA NOOK** | MIL RANGE | 123.05 | AG RADIO |
| **DONCASTER** | CIV AF | AG RADIO | |
| | | 120.35 | FINNINGLEY APP |
| **SANDTOFT** | CIV AF | 130.425 | AG RADIO |
| | | 120.35 | FINNINGLEY RAD / MATZ |
| **COWICK HALL** | PRI AF | 130.65 | AG RADIO |
| **FINNINGLEY** | MIL AF | 122.1 | TWR |
| | | 120.35 | APP / MATZ / LARS |
| | | 123.3 | PAR RADAR |
| | | *379.55* | *TWR* |
| | | *340.175* | *GRND* |
| | | *277.675TIS* | |
| | | *358.775* | *APP* |
| | | *285.125* | *DIR / MATZ / LARS* |
| | | *315.5* | *DIR* |
| | | *344.0* | *DIR* |
| | | *383.5* | *PAR RADAR* |
| | | *385.4* | *PAR RADAR* |
| **GAMSTON (RETFORD)** | CIV AF | 130.475 | AG RADIO |
| **STURGATE** | CIV AF | 130.3 | AG RADIO |
| | | 127.35 | WADDINGTON APP |
| **WICKENBY** | CIV AF | 122.45 | AG RADIO |
| | | 127.35 | WADDINGTON APP |
| **SCAMPTON** | MIL AF | 122.1 | TWR |
| | | 125.35 | WADDINGTON MATZ |
| | | 123.3 | PAR RADAR |
| | | *282.4* | *TWR* |
| | | *257.8* | *TWR* |
| | | *372.5* | *GRND* |
| | | *312.5* | *WADDINGTON APP / RAD* |
| | | *362.3* | *WADDINGTON APP / RAD* |
| | | *249.85* | *DEPARTURES* |
| | | *362.3* | *DEPARTURES* |

# AREA 7

## AIRFIELDS OF HUMBERSIDE, E. MIDLANDS & LINCS.

| STATION | TYPE | FREQUENCY | SERVICE / REMARKS / CALL |
|---|---|---|---|
| **SCAMPTON (continued)** | | *357.05* | *RECOVERIES* |
| | | *344.0* | *RECOVERIES* |
| | | *357.1* | *PAR RADAR* |
| | | *341.925* | *PAR RADAR* |
| **CONINGSBY** | MIL AF | 122.1 | TWR / APP / GRND |
| | | 120.8 | APP / GRND / MATZ |
| | | 123.3 | PAR RADAR |
| | | *257.875* | *TWR* |
| | | *358.55* | *GRND* |
| | | *312.225* | *APP / MATZ* |
| | | *362.3* | *APP* |
| | | *344.625* | *APP* |
| | | *262.95* | *DIR* |
| | | *344.0* | *DIR* |
| | | *300.925* | *PAR RADAR* |
| | | *337.975* | *PAR RADAR* |
| **WADDINGTON** | MIL AF | 122.1 | TWR |
| | | 127.35 | APP / MATZ / LARS |
| | | 123.3 | DIR / DEPARTURES |
| | | 125.35 | RAD / SRE |
| | | *285.05* | *TWR* |
| | | *257.8* | *TWR* |
| | | *342.125* | *GRND* |
| | | *244.275* | *OPS* |
| | | *312.5* | *APP / RAD* |
| | | *362.3* | *APP* |
| | | *300.575* | *DIR* |
| | | *249.85* | *DEPARTURES* |
| | | *344.0* | *DIR* |
| | | *296.75* | *RAD / LARS* |
| | | *309.675* | *PAR RADAR* |
| | | *385.4* | *PAR RADAR* |
| **TEMPLE BRUER** | PRI AF | 119.0 | CRANWELL APP |
| | | 127.35 | WADDINGTON APP |
| **CRANWELL** | MIL AF | 122.1 | TWR / APP |
| | | 119.0 | APP / MATZ |
| | | 123.3 | DIR / PAR RADAR |
| | | *379.525* | *TWR* |
| | | *257.8* | *TWR* |
| | | *297.9* | *GRND* |

# AREA 7

## AIRFIELDS OF HUMBERSIDE, E. MIDLANDS & LINCS.

| STATION | TYPE | FREQUENCY | SERVICE / REMARKS / CALL |
|---|---|---|---|
| **CRANWELL (Continued)** | | *340.475* | *APP* |
| | | *362.3* | *APP* |
| | | *250.05* | *ZONE* |
| | | *282.0* | *DIR* |
| | | *344.0* | *DIR* |
| | | *383.475* | *PAR RADAR* |
| | | *285.15* | *PAR RADAR* |
| **CRANWELL NORTH** | MIL AF | —— | GLIDER OPS ONLY |
| **BARKSTON HEATH** | MIL AF | 119.0 | MATZ |
| | | *342.075* | *TWR* |
| | | *340.475* | *CRANWELL APP* |
| **NOTTINGHAM** | CIV AF | 122.8 | AG RADIO |
| | | 119.65 | EAST MIDLANDS APP |
| **COAL ASTON** . | PRI AF | 124.6 | LONDON INFORMATION |
| **NETHERTHORPE** | CIV AF | 123.275 | AG RADIO / AFIS |
| **HUCKNALL** | PRI AF | 130.8 | AG RADIO |
| **EAST MIDLANDS** | CIV AP | 124.0 | TWR / RAD / SRE |
| | | 121.9 | GRND |
| | | 128.225 | ATIS |
| | | 119.65 | APP |
| | | 120.125 | RAD / SRE |
| **DERBY** | CIV AF | 118.35 | AG RADIO |
| | | 119.65 | EAST MIDLANDS APP |
| **NEWTON** | MIL AF | 122.1 | TWR / APP |
| | | *375.425* | *TWR* |
| | | *257.8* | *TWR* |
| | | *251.725* | *APP* |
| | | *362.3* | *RAD* |
| **LEICESTER** | CIV AF | 122.125 | AG RADIO |
| **LANGAR** | PRI AF | 129.9 | LANGAR DZ |
| | | 130.2 | COTTISMORE APP |
| **SPANHOE** | PRI AF | 130.2 | COTTISMORE APP |
| | | 122.1 | WITTERING TWR |
| **COTTESMORE** | MIL AF | 122.1 | TWR / GRND |
| | | 123.3 | WITTERING APP |
| | | 130.2 | TWR / APP / MATZ / LARS |

# AREA 7

## AIRFIELDS OF HUMBERSIDE, E. MIDLANDS & LINCS.

| STATION | TYPE | FREQUENCY | SERVICE / REMARKS / CALL |
|---|---|---|---|
| **COTTESMORE (Continued)** | | 119.0 | APP / MATZ |
| | | 123.3 | PAR RADAR / SRE |
| | | 370.05 | TWR |
| | | 257.8 | TWR |
| | | 312.075 | DIR / APP |
| | | 340.575 | APP / LARS |
| | | 380.95 | WITTERING APP |
| | | 376.575 | DEPARTURE CONTROL |
| | | 358.725 | DIR / MATZ |
| | | 376.575 | IR |
| | | 262.9 | PAR RADAR |
| | | 337.875 | PAR RADAR |
| **STRUBBY** | PRI AF | 122.375 | AG RADIO |
| | | 130.1 | GLIDERS |
| | | 3453 kHZ | SSB RADIO |
| **SKEGNESS (INGOLDMELLS)** | CIV AF | 130.45 | AG RADIO |

# AREA 8

## ZONES & AIRWAYS OF EAST MIDLANDS

| FREQUENCY | CALL | SERVICE |
|---|---|---|
| 134.7 | LONDON INFORMATION | NORTH OF FIR |
| 124.6 | LONDON INFORMATION | SOUTH OF FIR |
| 131.05 | LONDON INFORMATION | NORTH OF UIR |
| 132.6 | LONDON INFORMATION | SOUTH OF UIR |
| 135.275 | LONDON MIL (NORTH) | RADAR & INFORMATION |
| 135.275 | LONDON MIL (NORTH) | UPPER AIRSPACE INFORMATION |
| 299.975 | LONDON MIL (NORTH) | UPPER AIRSPACE INFORMATION |
| 126.6 | VOLMET BROADCAST | VOLMET NORTH |
| 135.375 | OLMET BROADCAST | VOLMET MAIN |
| 125.275 | ANGLIA RADAR | RADAR & INFORMATION |
| 128.925 | ANGLIA RADAR | RADAR & INFORMATION |

# AREA 8

## AIRFIELDS OF THE COUNTIES NORTH OF LONDON

| STATION | TYPE | FREQUENCY | SERVICE / REMARKS / CALL |
|---------|------|-----------|--------------------------|
| **FENLAND** | CIV AF | 122.925 | AG RADIO. AFIS |
| **LEICESTER** | CIV AF | 122.125 | AG RADIO |
| **BRUNTINGTHORPE** | CIV AF | 122.825 | AG RADIO |
| **CROWLAND** | PRI AF | 130.2 | COTTISMORE APP |
| **WITTERING** | MIL AF | 122.1 | TWR |
| | | 142.29 | TWR / APP |
| | | 130.2 | APP / MATZ |
| | | 123.3 | PAR RADAR |
| | | *357.15* | *TWR* |
| | | *257.8* | *TWR* |
| | | *311.95* | *GRND* |
| | | *380.95* | *BASE APP* |
| | | *362.3* | *BASE APP* |
| | | *376.575* | *DEPARTURE CONTROL* |
| | | *344.0* | *DEPARTURE CONTROL* |
| | | *383.225* | *PAR RADAR* |
| | | *337.95* | *PAR RADAR* |
| **LITTLE GRANSDEN** | CIV AF | 130.85 | AG RADIO |
| **DEENETHORPE** | CIV AF | 127.575 | AG RADIO |
| | | 130.20 | COTTISMORE APP |
| **NORTHAMPTON (SYWELL)** | CIV AF | 122.7 | AG RADIO |
| **SIBSON** | CIV AF | 122.3 | AG RADIO |
| **CONNINGTON** | CIV AF | 129.725 | AG RADIO |
| | | 134.05 | WYTON APP |
| **ALCONBURY** | MIL USAAF | 125.35 | TWR |
| | | 122.1 | TWR |
| | | 134.05 | WYTON APP |
| | | *383.45* | *TWR* |
| | | *257.8* | *TWR* |
| | | *259.825* | *GRND* |
| | | *231.175* | *ATIS* |
| | | *362.3* | *WYTON APP* |
| | | *372.525* | *DEPARTURES* |
| | | *342.225* | *DISPATCHER* |
| | | *340.125* | *COMMAND POST* |
| | | *257.75* | *METRO* |
| | | *RADAR/PAR FREQUENCIES AS DIRECTED* | |

# AREA 8

## AIRFIELDS OF THE COUNTIES NORTH OF LONDON

| STATION | TYPE | FREQUENCY | SERVICE / REMARKS / CALL |
|---------|------|-----------|--------------------------|
| **WYTON** | MIL AF | 122.1 | TWR |
| | | 134.05 | APP / MATZ / LARS |
| | | 123.3 | PAR RADAR |
| | | *312.275* | *TWR* |
| | | *257.8* | *TWR* |
| | | *293.65* | *GRND* |
| | | *249.55* | *APP* |
| | | *344.0* | *APP* |
| | | *375.525* | *DEPARTURES* |
| | | *362.375* | *APP / LARS* |
| | | *362.3* | *APP* |
| | | *292.9* | *PAR RAD* |
| | | *385.4* | *PAR RAD* |
| **MARHAM** | MIL AF | 122.1 | TWR |
| | | 124.15 | APP / RAD / MATZ / LARS |
| | | 123.3 | PAR RADAR |
| | | *337.9* | *TWR* |
| | | *257.8* | *TWR* |
| | | *336.35* | *GRND* |
| | | *312.55* | *OPS* |
| | | *291.95* | *APP / LARS* |
| | | *362.3* | *APP* |
| | | *293.775* | *RAD* |
| | | *344.0* | *RAD* |
| | | *379.65* | *PAR RADAR* |
| | | *385.4* | *PAR RADAR* |
| **BOUGHTON** | PRI AF | 124.15 | MARHAM APP |
| **CAMBRIDGE** | CIV AF | 122.2 | TWR |
| | | 123.6 | APP |
| | | 130.75 | RAD / SRE |
| | | 372.425 | TWR / RAD |
| **BOURN** | PRI AF | 129.8 | AG RADIO |
| **FOWLMERE** | CIV AF | 120.925 | AG RADIO |
| | | 125.55 | STANSTED APP |
| | | 122.075 | DUXFORD INFO |
| **OLD WARDEN** | PRI AF | 123.05 | AG ON DISPLAY DAYS |
| **CRANFIELD** | PRI AF | 123.2 | TWR |
| | | 121.875 | ATIS |

# AREA 8

## AIRFIELDS OF THE COUNTIES NORTH OF LONDON

| STATION | TYPE | FREQUENCY | SERVICE / REMARKS / CALL |
|---|---|---|---|
| **CRANFIELD (Continued)** | | 122.85 | TWR / APP / RAD |
| | | 362.15 | TWR / APP /RAD |
| **DUXFORD** | PRI AF | 122.075 | AG RADIO |
| **DUNSTABLE** | PRI AF | 129.55 | LUTON APP |
| LUTON | CIV AP | 132.55 | TWR |
| | | 121.75 | GRND |
| | | 120.575 | ATIS. ARR / DEP INFO |
| | | 129.55 | APP / LARS |
| | | 128.75 | APP |
| | | 126.725 | APP / RAD |
| | | 121.6 | FIRE |
| | | 259.875 | LARS |
| **LONDON. STANSTED** | CIV AP | 123.8 | TWR |
| | | 121.725 | GRND |
| | | 127.175 | ATIS. ARR / DEP INFO |
| | | 125.55 | APP / RAD |
| **HIGH EASTER** | PRI AF | 125.55 | STANSTED APP |

# AREA 8A

## ZONES & AIRWAYS NORTH EAST OF LONDON

| FREQUENCY | CALL | SERVICE |
|---|---|---|
| 124.6 | LONDON INFORMATION | SOUTH OF FIR |
| 132.6 | LONDON INFORMATION | SOUTH OF UIR |
| 135.275 | LONDON MIL | INFORMATION & RADAR |
| 299.975 | LONDON MIL | INFORMATION & RADAR |
| 291.8 | LJAO | LONDON JOINT UIR. |
| 126.6 | VOLMET BROADCAST | VOLMET NORTH |
| 135.375 | VOLMET BROADCAST | VOLMET MAIN |
| 125.275 | ANGLIA RADAR | RADAR & INFORMATION |
| 128.925 | ANGLIA RADAR | RADAR & INFORMATION |
| 118.475 | LONDON CONTROL | AIRWAYS—R1, R12, R123, R126, UA37, UB29, UB317, UR1, UR12, UR123, UR126. |

# AREA 8A

## ZONES & AIRWAYS NORTH EAST OF LONDON

| FREQUENCY | CALL | SERVICE |
|---|---|---|
| 127.425 | LONDON CONTROL | AIRWAYS—UA1, UA2, UB3, UB4, UB29, UB39, UG1, UG45, UG106, UL1, UR1, UR8, UR12, UR29, UR37, UR41,UR84, UR123, UA20,UA27, UA34, UA37, UA47, U8A30, UB11, UB39, UB71, UB295, UG39, UG45 |
| 127.95 | LONDON CONTROL | AIRWAYS—B317, B29, R1, R12, R123, R126, UA37, UB29, UB317, UG39, UR1, UR12, UR123 UR126, |
| 128.425 | LONDON CONTROL | AIRWAYS—A2, A20, B3, B4, B317, R8, UA2, UB3, UA20, UA30, UB4, UG1, UG106, UL1, UR37, |
| 129.6 | LONDON CONTROL | AIRWAYS—B317, B29, R1, R12, R123, R126, UA37, UB317, UG39 UR1, UR12, UR123, UR126, |
| 132.45 | LONDON CONTROL | AIRWAYS—A2, UA2, UB4, |
| 133.45 | LONDON CONTROL | AIRWAYS—R1, R12, R123, UB317, UR1, UR12, UR123, |
| 133.525 | LONDON CONTROL | AIRWAYS—B1, B5, R1, R12, R123,UB1, UA37, UB5, UR1, UR4, UR12, UR123, UR126, UB29, UB105, UB317, UG39, |
| 133.525 | LONDON CONTROL | AIRWAYS—B1, B5, R1, R12, R123,UB1, UA37, UB5, UR1, UR4, UR12, UR123, UR126, UB29, UB105, UB317, UG39, |
| 134.45 | LONDON CONTROL | AIRWAYS—A2, R37, UA2, UB4, |
| 134.75 | LONDON CONTROL | AIRWAYS—UA1, UA2, UA.34, UA30, UA47, UB29, UB39, UB295, UG1, UG39, UR1, UR12, UR123, UR4, UR8, UR37, |
| 136.275 | LONDON CONTROL | AIRWAYS—B4, B5, R1, R12, R123, UB1, UB5, UB29, UB29, UB317, UB105, UR1. UR12, UR123,   UR4, UR126, |
| 136.55 | LONDON CONTROL | AIRWAYS—B317, B29, R1, R12, R123, UA37, UB29, UB317, UR1, UR12, UR123, UR126. |

# AREA 8A

## AIRFIELDS OF ANGLIA & COUNTIES NE. OF LONDON

| STATION | TYPE | FREQUENCY | SERVICE / REMARKS / CALL |
|---|---|---|---|
| GREAT MASSINGHAM | PRI AF | 124.15 | MARHAM APP |
| SHIPDHAM | CIV AF | 119.55 | AG RADIO |
| LITTLE SNORING | CIV AF | 124.15 | MARHAM APP |
| CROMER | PRI AF | 129.825 | AG RADIO |
| COLTISHALL | MIL AF | 142.29 | TWR |
| | | 122.1 | TWR / APP |
| | | 125.9 | APP / MATZ / LARS |
| | | 123.5 | |
| | | *339.95* | *TWR* |
| | | *296.725* | *GRND* |
| | | *364.8* | *OPS* |
| | | *379.275* | *APP / MATZ* |
| | | *342.25* | *DIR / APP* |
| | | *293.425* | *DIR / APP / LARS* |
| | | *275.975* | *PAR RADAR* |
| | | *254.25* | *PAR RADAR* |
| LUDHAM | CIV AF | 119.35 | NORWICH APP |
| BACTON | CIV AF | 123.45 | AG RADIO |
| FELTHORPE | PRI AF | 123.5 | AG RADIO |
| NORWICH | CIV AP | 124.25 | TWR |
| | | 119.35 | APP / RAD |
| | | 128.325 | RAD / SRE |
| NORTH DENES | CIV AF | 123.4 | TWR / APP |
| | | 3453 KHz | (SSB TRANSMISSIONS) |
| | | 5645 KHz | (SSB TRANSMISSIONS) |
| SOUTH BURLINGHAM | PRI AF | 119.35 | NORWICH APP |
| | | 125.9 | COLTISHALL APP |
| SWANTON MORELY | MIL AF | 123.5 | AG RADIO |
| BECCLES | CIV AF | 134.6 | AG RADIO |
| FOULSHAM | PRI AF | 130.65 | AG RADIO |
| HETHEL | PRI AF | 122.35 | AG RADIO |
| SEETHING | PRI AF | 122.6 | AG RADIO |
| TIBENHAM | CIV AF | 129.975 | AG RADIO |
| | | 130.1 | GLIDERS |
| STANFORD | MIL STN | 307.8 | ARMY AG RADIO |

# AREA 8A

## AIRFIELDS OF ANGLIA & COUNTIES NE. OF LONDON

| STATION | TYPE | FREQUENCY | SERVICE / REMARKS / CALL |
|---|---|---|---|
| **HETHERSET** | PRI AF | 129.825 | AG RADIO |
| **MILDENHALL** | MIL AF | 122.55 | TWR |
| | | 142.075 | LAKENHEATH DEPS |
| | | *258.825* | *TWR* |
| | | *398.35* | *APP / LARS* |
| | | *380.15* | *GRND* |
| | | *277.075* | *ATIS* |
| | | *398.35* | *APP / GCA* |
| | | *365.1* | *OPS / DISPATCHER* |
| | | *312.45* | *COMMAND POST* |
| | | *344.8* | *COMMAND POST* |
| | | *242.075* | *LAKENHEATH DEPS* |
| **LAKENHEATH** | MIL AF | 122.1 | TWR |
| | | 128.9 | APP / MATZ |
| | | 137.2 | APP |
| | | 123.3 | PAR RADAR / SRE |
| | | *358.675* | *TWR* |
| | | *257.8* | *TWR* |
| | | *397.975* | *GRND* |
| | | *249.7* | *ATIS* |
| | | *257.76* | *MILDENHALL METRO* |
| | | *300.825* | *OPS / DISPATCHER* |
| | | *269.075* | *COMMAND POST* |
| | | *242.075* | *APP* |
| | | *398.35* | *APP* |
| | | *309.75* | *PAR RADAR* |
| | | *290.825* | *PAR RADAR* |
| | | *388.675* | *PAR RADAR* |
| | | *264.1* | *PAR RADAR* |
| | | *279.250* | *PAR RADAR* |
| **NEWMARKET** | PRI AF | 129.05 | HONNINGTON APP |
| **CROWFIELD** | PRI AF | 122.775 | AG RADIO |
| **WATTISHAM** | MIL AF | 122.1 | TWR |
| | | 129.975 | AG / ANGLIA BASE |
| | | 124.925 | APP |
| | | 123.3 | DIR / PAR RADAR |
| | | *343.425* | *TWR* |
| | | *291.125* | *APP* |
| | | *283.575* | *DIR* |
| | | *356.175* | *PAR RADAR* |
| | | *359.825* | *PAR RADAR* |

# AREA 8A

## AIRFIELDS OF ANGLIA & COUNTIES NE. OF LONDON

| STATION | TYPE | FREQUENCY | SERVICE / REMARKS / CALL |
|---|---|---|---|
| **IPSWICH** | CIV AP | 118.325 | TWR / APP / RAD |
| NUTHAMPSTEAD | PRI AF | 123.05 | AG RADIO |
| AUDLEY END | PRI AF | 122.35 | AG RADIO |
| EARLS COLNE | PRI AF | 122.425 | AG RADIO |
| **CLACTON** | CIV AF | 122.325 | AG RADIO |

# AMENDMENTS

| STATION | TYPE | FREQUENCY | SERVICE / REMARKS / CALL |
|---|---|---|---|

# AREAS 9 & 9A

## ZONES & AIRWAYS OF LONDON & SE. ENGLAND

| FREQUENCY | CALL | SERVICE |
|---|---|---|
| 124.6 | LONDON INFORMATION | SOUTH OF FIR |
| 132.6 | LONDON INFORMATION | SOUTH OF UIR |
| 135.275 | LONDON MIL | INFORMATION & RADAR |
| 299.975 | LONDON MIL | INFORMATION & RADAR |
| 291.8 | LJAO | LONDON JOINT UIR. |
| 126.6 | VOLMET BROADCAST | VOLMET NORTH |
| 135.375 | VOLMET BROADCAST | VOLMET MAIN |
| 120.175 | LONDON CONTROL | INBOUND FROM SOUTH |
| 121.325 | LONDON CONTROL | INBOUND & OUTBOUND TO & FROM SW. |
| 129.075 | LONDON CONTROL | INBOUND & OUTBOUND TO & FROM SW. |
| 125.95 | LONDON CONTROL | INBOUND FROM NORTH & NE. |
| 121.225 | LONDON CONTROL | (USED AS DIRECTED BY ATCC) |
| 121.725 | LONDON CONTROL | INBOUND FROM NORTH & NW. |
| 129.275 | LONDON CONTROL | (USED AS DIRECTED BY ATCC) |
| 130.925 | LONDON CONTROL | INBOUND FROM EAST |
| 133.175 | LONDON CONTROL | (USED AS DIRECTED BY ATCC) |
| 119.775 | LONDON CONTROL | DEPARTURES TO NORTH WEST |
| 118.825 | LONDON CONTROL | DEPARTURES TO NORTH |
| 120.525 | LONDON CONTROL | DEPARTURES TO SOUTH EAST |
| 133.975 | LONDON CONTROL | (USED AS DIRECTED BY ATCC) |
| 134.125 | LONDON CONTROL | (USED AS DIRECTED BY ATCC), |
| 136.575 | LONDON CONTROL | (USED AS DIRECTED BY ATCC) |
| 135.15 | LONDON RADAR | LONDON MILITARY SOUTH |
| 275.475 | LONDON RADAR | LONDON MILITARY SOUTH |
| 118.475 | LONDON CONTROL | AIRWAYS—R1, R12, R123, R126, UA37, UB29, UB317, UR1, UR12, UR123, UR126. |
| 120.025 | LONDON CONTROL | AIRWAYS—B321, R1, R41, R84, UB11, UR1, UR12, UR123, UR8, UR24, UR37, UR41, UR84. |
| 124.275 | LONDON CONTROL | AIRWAYS—A1, A47, A56, A34, B11, G27, R1, R8, R41, R84, R803, UA1, UA34, UB11, UR1, UR12, UR123, UR8, UR25, UR37. |
| 126.075 | LONDON CONTROL | AIRWAYS—A25, B1, G4D, R8, W2D, U8A25, UA29, UG4, UG45, UL772, UR8, UR14, UR37, UR40, UR72, UR116, UR168, UT7, UR3. UN862, UN863, UN865, UR4, |

# AREAS 9 & 9A

## ZONES & AIRWAYS OF LONDON & SE. ENGLAND

| FREQUENCY | CALL | SERVICE |
|---|---|---|
| 127.425 | LONDON CONTROL | AIRWAYS—UA1, UA2, UB3, UB4, UB29, UB39, UG1, UG45, UG106, UL1, UR1, UR8, UR12, UR29, UR37, UR41, UR84, UR123, UA20, UA27, UA34, UA37, UA47, U8A30, UB11, UB39, UB71,UB295, UG39, UG45 |
| 128.425 | LONDON CONTROL | AIRWAYS—A2, A20, B3, B4, B317, R8, UA2, UB3, UA20, UA30, UB4, UG1, UG106, UL1, UR37, |
| 129.6 | LONDON CONTROL | AIRWAYS—B317, B29, R1, R12, R123, R126, UA37, UB317, UG39, UR1, UR12, UR123, UR126, |
| 131.125 | LONDON CONTROL | AIRWAYS—A1, A20, A47, B3, B4, B317, B321, R41, UA1, UA2, UA34, UB3, UA 47, UB4, UB71, UB317, UR41, |
| 131.2 | LONDON CONTROL | AIRWAYS—G1, B10, R14, R41, UA29, UP2, UR41, UR14, UB10, UN546 |
| 132.95 | LONDON CONTROL | AIRWAYS—UG4, UG45, UL772, UA29, UT7, UR168, UR40, UR8, UR116, UR72, UR37, |
| 133.525 | LONDON CONTROL | AIRWAYS—B1, B5, R1, R12, R123,UB1, UA37, UB5, UR1, UR4, UR12, UR123, UR126, UB29, UB105, UB317, UG39, |
| 133.7 | LONDON CONTROL | AIRWAYS—A1, A2, A20, A47, B3, B4, R41, B317, B321, UA1, UA2, UA34, UA47, UB3, UB4, UB71, UB317, UR41, |
| 134.25 | LONDON CONTROL | AIRWAYS—B1, B5, UA37, UB1, UB5, UB105, UL7, UL74, UR4, |
| 134.75 | LONDON CONTROL | AIRWAYS—UA1, UA2, UA.34, UA30, UA47, UB29, UB39, UB295, UG1, UG39, UR1, UR12, UR123, UR4, UR8, UR37, |
| 134.9 | LONDON CONTROL | AIRWAYS—B3, B4, B317, R8, UB3, UB71, UG1, UG106, UL1, UR37, |
| 135.05 | LONDON CONTROL | AIRWAYS—A47, R37, UA47, UB4, UN862, UN863, UN865, |
| 135.325 | LONDON CONTROL | AIRWAYS—A1, A34, A47, A56, B11, R1, R803, UA1, UA34, UB11, UR1, UR12, UR123, R84, UR41, UR8, UR24, UR25, UR37, UR84. |
| 136.2 | LONDON CONTROL | AIRWAYS—A1, A2, A20, A47, B1, R101, W2D, UA1, UA2, UB4, |

# AREAS 9 & 9A

## ZONES & AIRWAYS OF LONDON & SE. ENGLAND

| FREQUENCY | CALL | SERVICE |
|---|---|---|
| 136.275 | LONDON CONTROL | AIRWAYS—B4, B5, R1, R12, R123, UB1, UB5, UB29, UB29, UB317, UB105, UR1. UR12, UR123, UR4, UR126. |
| 136.55 | LONDON CONTROL | AIRWAYS—B317, B29, R1, R12, R123, UA37, UB29, UB317, UR1, UR12, UR123, UR126, |
| 136.6 | LONDON CONTROL | AIRWAYS—A1, A47, A56, A34, B11, G27, R1, R8, R41, R84, R803, UA1, UA1, UA34, UB11, UR8, UR37, UR25, |

# AREA 9

## AIRFIELDS OF HOME COUNTIES & GREATER LONDON

| STATION | TYPE | FREQUENCY | SERVICE / REMARKS / CALL |
|---|---|---|---|
| **ANDREWSFIELD** | CIV AF | 130.55 | AG RADIO |
| | | 122.55 | STANSTED APP |
| *SOUTHEND* | CIV AP | 127.725 | TWR |
| | | 121.8 | ATIS. DEPARTURES |
| | | 128.95 | APP / RAD |
| **NORTH WEALD** | CIV AF | 123.525 | AG RADIO |
| | | 129.975 | GLIDERS |
| | | 130.175 | ACEAIR |
| **RUSH GREEN (HITCHIN)** | CIV AF | 122.35 | AG RADIO |
| **PANSHANGER** | CIV AF | 120.25 | AG RADIO |
| **STAPLEFORD** | CIV AF | 122.6 | AG RADIO |
| | | 122.05 | AEROMEGA OPS |
| **HALTON** | MIL AF | 130.425 | AG RADIO (CLUB FREQ) |
| | | *356.275* | *AG RADIO* |
| **SHENDISH (FELDEN)** | PRI HELIPAD | 129.75 | AIRTOUR RADIO |
| **ELSTREE** | CIV AF | 122.4 | AG RADIO |

# AREA 9

## AIRFIELDS OF HOME COUNTIES & GREATER LONDON

| STATION | TYPE | FREQUENCY | SERVICE / REMARKS / CALL |
|---|---|---|---|
| **LONDON CITY** | CIV AP | 119.425 | TWR |
| | | 118.075 | TWR |
| | | 132.7 | APP THAMES RADAR |
| | | 128.025 | CITY RADAR |
| **LONDON BATTERSEA** | CIV HELIPAD | 122.9 | TWR |
| | | 119.9 | APP |
| **MET POLICE** | | 130.47 | AG RADIO |
| **LONDON HAYES** | PRI HELIPAD | 123.65 | AG RADIO |
| **LONDON NORTHOLT** | MIL AF | 126.45 | TWR / APP |
| | | 124.975 | DIR / GRND |
| | | 120.325 | DIR / SRE |
| | | 119.20 | HEATHROW APP |
| | | 130.35 | DIRECTOR / PAR RAD |
| | | 120.325 | DIRECTOR / PAR RAD |
| | | 128.9 | LONDON CONTROL |
| | | 125.8 | LONDON CONTROL |
| | | 125.95 | LONDON CONTROL |
| | | 125.55 | STANSTED ZONE |
| | | *312.35* | *TWR* |
| | | *257.8* | *TWR* |
| | | *244.425* | *OPS* |
| | | *344.975* | *APP* |
| | | *362.3* | *APP* |
| | | *379.425* | *DIR* |
| | | *375.5* | *PAR RADAR* |
| | | *385.4* | *PAR RADAR* |
| **LONDON HEATHROW** | CIV AP | 118.7 | TWR |
| | | 118.5 | TWR |
| | | 124.475 | TWR (AS INSTRUCTED) |
| | | 121.9 | GRND |
| | | 121.7 | GRND |
| | | 121.975 | GRND.DEP INITIAL CALL |
| | | 133.075 | ATIS. ARR / DEP |
| | | 119.725 | DIRECTOR / APP |
| | | 135.125 | DIRECTOR / APP |
| | | 127.525 | DIRECTOR / APP |
| | | 134.975 | DIRECTOR / APP /RAD |
| | | 119.725 | RAD |
| | | 125.625 | RAD |

# AREA 9

## AIRFIELDS OF HOME COUNTIES & GREATER LONDON

| STATION | TYPE | FREQUENCY | SERVICE / REMARKS / CALL |
|---|---|---|---|
| **LONDON HEATHROW** (Continued) | | 135.125 | RAD (AS INSTRUCTED |
| | | 119.9 | RAD (SPEC VFR & HELIS) |
| | | 121.6 | FIRE |
| **THAME** | PRI AF | 124.6 | LONDON INFORMATION |
| **DENHAM** | CIV AF | 130.725 | AG RADIO |
| **WYCOMBE AIR PARK** | CIV AF | 126.55 | AG RADIO |
| | | 121.775 | GRND |
| **WHITE WALTHAM** | CIV AF | 122.6 | AG RADIO |

# AREA 9A

## AIRFIELDS OF HOME COUNTIES SOUTH OF LONDON

| STATION | TYPE | FREQUENCY | SERVICE / REMARKS / CALL |
|---|---|---|---|
| **MANSTON** | MIL AF | 128.775 | TWR |
| | | 119.275 | TWR |
| | | 122.1 | TWR / APP |
| | | 126.35 | APP / RAD / LARS |
| | | 123.3 | PAR RADAR |
| | | *344.35* | *TWR* |
| | | *257.8* | *TWR* |
| | | *379.025* | *APP / LARS* |
| | | *362.3* | *APP* |
| | | *338.625* | *DIR / RAD* |
| | | *344.0* | *DIR /RAD* |
| | | *312.325* | *PAR RADAR* |
| | | *385.4* | *PAR RADAR* |
| **ROCHESTER** | PRI AF | 122.25 | AFIS |
| **WEST MALLING** | CIV AF | 130.875 | AG RADIO |
| **BIGGIN HILL** | CIV AF | 134.8 | TWR |
| | | 121.875 | ATIS |
| | | 129.4 | APP |
| | | 132.7 | THAMES RADAR |
| **REDHILL** | CIV AF | 120.275 | TWR / AFIS |

# AREA 9A

## AIRFIELDS OF HOME COUNTIES SOUTH OF LONDON

| STATION | TYPE | FREQUENCY | SERVICE / REMARKS / CALL |
|---|---|---|---|
| **FAIROAKS** | CIV AF | 123.425 | AG RADIO / AFIS |
| **BLACKBUSHE** | CIV AF | 122.3 | AFIS |
| | | 125.25 | FARNBOROUGH APP |
| | | 130.37 | AIR HANSON OPS |
| **FARNBOROUGH** | MOD AF | 122.5 | TWR |
| | | 129.975 | AG RADIO (GLIDERS) |
| | | 134.35 | APP / PAR RADAR |
| | | 125.25 | ATC / RAD / LARS |
| | | 130.375 | FARNBO' EXECUTIVE |
| | | 130.35 | APP / PAR RADAR |
| | | *357.4* | *TWR* |
| | | *336.275* | *APP / LARS* |
| | | *386.775* | *APP / ODIHAM RAD* |
| | | *315.525* | *APP / RAD* |
| | | *259.0* | *PAR RADAR* |
| **ODIHAM** | MIL AF | 122.1 | TWR / APP |
| | | 125.25 | FARNBO' APP / MATZ |
| | | *309.625* | *TWR* |
| | | *257.8* | *TWR* |
| | | *276.175* | *ATIS* |
| | | *315.975* | *APP* |
| | | *362.3* | *APP* |
| | | *386.775* | *RAD / SHE* |
| | | *300.45* | *PAR RADAR* |
| | | *385.4* | *PAR RADAR* |
| **POPHAM** | CIV AF | 129.8 | AG RADIO |

# AREA 9A

## AIRFIELDS OF SOUTH EAST & CENTRAL S. COAST

| STATION | TYPE | FREQUENCY | SERVICE / REMARKS / CALL |
|---|---|---|---|
| CANTERBURY | PRI AF | 126.35 | MANSTON APP |
| LYDD | CIV AF | 120.7 | TWR / APP / AG RADIO |
| | | 131.3 | TWR |
| DEANLAND | PRI AF | 129.725 | AG RADIO |
| LASHENDEN (HEADCORN) | CIV AF | 122.0 | AG RADIO |
| DUNSFOLD | PRI AF | 124.325 | TWR |
| | | 122.55 | APP / RAD |
| | | 135.175 | APP / RAD / LARS |
| | | 375.4 | TWR |
| | | *367.375* | *APP / LARS* |
| | | *312.625* | *APP / RAD* |
| *LONDON GATWICK* | CIV AP | 124.225 | TWR |
| | | 134.225 | TWR |
| | | 121.8 | GRND |
| | | 128.475 | ATIS DEPARTURES |
| | | 121.95 | INITIAL DEP CALL |
| | | 126.825 | DIRECTOR / APP |
| | | 129.025 | DIRECTOR / APP |
| | | 135.575 | DIRECTOR / APP |
| | | 118.95 | DIRECTOR APP |
| | | ???.? | RADAR AS DIRECTED |
| LASHAM | PRI AF | 122.875 | AG RADIO |
| | | 129.90 | AG (GLIDER OPS) |
| | | 125.25 | FARNBOROUGH APP |
| SHOREHAM | CIV AF | 123.15 | TWR / APP / AG RADIO |
| | | 125.4 | TWR (AS DIRECTED) |
| | | 121.75 | ATIS |
| CHICHESTER (GOODWOOD) | CIV AF | 120.65 | TWR |
| | | 122.45 | TWR / APP / AG RADIO |
| | | 125.875 | DUNSFOLD APP / LARS |
| GOODWOOD RACECOURSE | PRI HELIPAD | 130.5 | AG RADIO |
| SOLENT AREA | | 120.225 | SOLENT APPROACH |
| *SOUTHAMPTON AIRPORT* | CIV AP | 118.2 | TWR |
| | | 113.35 | ATIS |

# AREA 9A

## AIRFIELDS OF SOUTH EAST & CENTRAL S. COAST

| STATION | TYPE | FREQUENCY | SERVICE / REMARKS / CALL |
|---|---|---|---|
| **SOUTHAMPTHON AIRPORT (Continued)** | | 131.0 | APP |
| | | 128.85 | APP / RAD |
| | | 120.225 | SOLENT APP |
| | | 121.6 | FIRE |
| **LEE ON SOLENT** | MIL AF | 135.7 | TWR |
| | | 132.65 | SAR |
| | | 3l5.65 | TWR |
| **FLEETLANDS** | MIL HELIPAD | 137.7 | AG (LEE TWR) |
| | | 315.65 | TWR AG (LEE TWR) |
| **BEMBRIDGE (IOW)** | PRI AF | 123.25 | AG RADIO |
| **SANDOWN (IOW)** | CIV AF | 123.5 | AG RADIO |

# AREA MAP

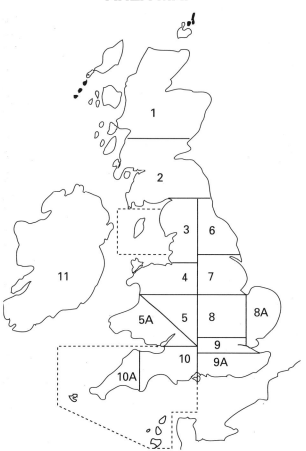

# AREAS 10 & 10A

## ZONES & AIRWAYS OF SW. ENGLAND & CHANNEL ISLANDS

| FREQUENCY | CALL | SERVICE |
|---|---|---|
| 124.6 | LONDON INFORMATION | SE OF FIR |
| 124.75 | LONDON INFORMATION | SW OF FIR |
| 131.05 | LONDON INFORMATION | SOUTH OF UIR |
| 135.15 | LONDON MIL | INFORMATION & RADAR |
| 275.475 | LONDON MIL | INFORMATION & RADAR |
| 291.8 | LJAO | LONDON JOINT UIR |
| 128.6 | VOLMET BROADCAST | VOLMET SOUTH |
| 135.375 | VOLMET BROADCAST | VOLMET MAIN |
| 125.2 | JERSEY ZONE | |
| 120.45 | JERSEY ZONE | |
| 124.275 | LONDON CONTROL | AIRWAYS—A1, A47, A56, A34, B11, G27, R1, R8, R41, R84, R803, UA1, UA34, UB11, UR1, UR12, UR123, UR8, UR25, UR37, |
| 125.2 | JERSEY ZONE | AIRWAYS—A25 |
| 126.075 | LONDON CONTROL | AIRWAYS—A25, B1, G4D, R8, W2D, U8A25, UA29, UG4, UG45, UL772, UR8, UR14, UR37, UR40, UR72, UR116, UR168, UT7, UR3. UN862, UN863, UN865, UR4, |
| 128.05 | LONDON CONTROL | AIRWAYS—A25, B3, B1, B53, B39. R3, W2D, W927D, UA34, UB1, UB3, UB39, |
| 131.2 | LONDON CONTROL | AIRWAYS—G1, B10, R14, R41, UA29, UP2, UR41, UR14, UB10, UN546 |
| 132. | LONDON CONTROL | AIRWAYS—R8, R37, UA25, UL722, UL1, UN862, UN863, UN865, UR72, UR168, UR14, UR116, UR40, UR8, UR37, UT7, |
| 132.95 | LONDON CONTROL | AIRWAYS—UG4, UG45, UL772, UA29, UT7, UR168, UR40, UR8, UR116, UR72, UR37, |
| 133.6 | LONDON CONTROL | AIRWAYS—B10, UB10, UB39, UB40, B321, UA25, UA29, UB29, UB295, UP2, |
| 134.25 | LONDON CONTROL | AIRWAYS—B1, B5, UA37, UB1, UB5, UB105, UL7, UL74, UR4, |
| 134.45 | LONDON CONTROL | AIRWAYS—A2, R37, UA2, UB4. |
| 135.05 | LONDON CONTROL | AIRWAYS—A47, R37, UA47, UB4, UN862, UN863, UN865, |
| 135.325 | LONDON CONTROL | AIRWAYS—A1, A34, A47, A56, B11, R1, R803, UA1, UA34, UB11, UR1, UR12, UR123, R84, UR41, UR8, UR24, UR25, UR37, UR84. |

# AREA 10

## AIRFIELDS OF SOUTH WESTERN COUNTIES

| STATION | TYPE | FREQUENCY | SERVICE / REMARKS / CALL |
|---|---|---|---|
| **NETHERAVON** | MIL AF | 128.3 | TWR DZ |
| | | *290.95* | *TWR* |
| | | *362.225* | *APP* |
| **SALISBURY PLAIN** | MIL NO FIELD | 122.75 | AG RADIO |
| | | 282.25 | AG RADIO |
| **THRUXTON** | CIV AF | 130.45 | AG RADIO |
| | | 126.7 | BOSCOMBE ZONE |
| **BOSCOMBE DOWN** | MOD AF | 130.75 | TWR |
| | | 130.75 | GRND |
| | | 135.15 | LONDON MIL SOUTH |
| | | 126.7 | APP / MATZ / LARS |
| | | 130.0 | PAR RADAR |
| | | *370.1* | *TWR* |
| | | *299.4* | *GRND* |
| | | *263.5* | *ATIS* |
| | | *291.65* | *APP / MATZ* |
| | | *380.025* | *APP / ZONE / LARS* |
| | | *276.85* | *PAR RADAR* |
| | | *381.125* | *PAR RADAR* |
| **MIDDLE WALLOP** | MIL AF | 122.1 | TWR / APP |
| | | 126.7 | APP / BOSCOMBE ZONE |
| | | *372.625* | *TWR* |
| | | *257.8* | *TWR* |
| | | *312.0* | *APP* |
| | | *312.675* | *DIR / APP* |
| | | *364.825* | *PAR RADAR* |
| **OLD SARUM** | CIV AF | 123.575 | AG RADIO |
| | | 123.2 | AG RADIO |
| | | 126.7 | BOSCOMBE ZONE |
| ***BOURNEMOUTH*** | CIV AP | 125.6 | TWR |
| ***AIRPORT*** | | 121.7 | GRND |
| | | 121.95 | ATIS DEPARTURES |
| | | 119.625 | APP / RAD |
| | | 118.65 | RAD |
| **COMPTON ABBAS** | CIV AF | 122.7 | AG RADIO / AFIS |
| **HENSTRIDGE** | PRI AF | 130.25 | AG RADIO |
| | | 127.35 | YEOVILTON APP |

# AREA 10A

## AIRFIELDS OF SOUTH WESTERN COUNTIES

| STATION | TYPE | FREQUENCY | SERVICE / REMARKS / CALL |
|---|---|---|---|
| **YEOVIL (JUDWIN)** | CIV AF | 125.4 | TWR / AG RADIO |
| | | 130.8 | APP / RAD |
| | | 127.35 | YEOVILTON RAD / MATZ |
| | | *372.425* | *TWR* |
| | | *369.975* | *APP / RAD* |
| **YEOVILTON** | MIL AF | 122.1 | TWR |
| | | 127.35 | APP / RAD / MATZ / LARS |
| | | 123.3 | PAR RADAR |
| | | 372.65 | TWR |
| | | 311.325 | GRND |
| | | *379.75* | *ATIS* |
| | | *362.3* | *APP* |
| | | *369.875* | *APP / MATZ / LARS* |
| | | *338.875* | *DIR* |
| | | *362.3* | *DIR* |
| | | *339.975* | *PAR RADAR* |
| | | *344.35* | *PAR ARDAR* |
| | | *8.977 KHz* | *AG RADIO / HF (SSB)* |
| **MERRYFIELD** | MIL AF | 122.1 | TWR |
| | | 312.7 | TWR |
| **PORTLAND** | MIL AF | 122.1 | TWR / APP / SRE |
| | | 123.3 | TWR / APP |
| | | 124.15 | TWR / APP / MATZ / SRE |
| | | *337.75* | *TWR* |
| | | *362.3* | *APP / PAR RADAR* |
| | | *300.175* | *APP / RAD / LARS* |
| | | *312.4* | *PAR RADAR* |
| | | *282.8* | *SAR AG RADIO* |
| | HF STN. | 6688 KHz | AG RADIO (SSB) |
| | HF STN | 6689.5 KHz | AG RADIO (SSB) |
| WESTON ZOYLAND | | PRI AF | |

## AIRFIELDS OF DEVON, CORNWALL & CHANNEL ISLANDS

| STATION | TYPE | FREQUENCY | SERVICE / REMARKS / CALL |
|---|---|---|---|
| **DUNKESWELL** | CIV AF | 123.475 | AG RADIO |
| *EXETER* | CIV AP | 119.8 | TWR |
| | | 128.15 | APP / RAD |
| | | 119.05 | RAD |
| **EAGLESCOTT** | CIV AF | 123.0 | AG RADIO |
| **DARTMOUTH** | MIL HELIPAD | 386.725 | RN COLLEGE |
| **CHIVENOR** | MIL AF | 122.1 | TWR / RAD / RESCUE |
| | | 130.2 | APP / MATZ / LARS |
| | | 123.3 | PAR RADAR |
| | | *362.45* | *TWR* |
| | | *379.925* | *GRND* |
| | | *340.0* | *APP / MATZ / LARS* |
| | | *364.775* | *APP* |
| | | *362.3* | *APP* |
| | | *376.675* | *DIR / APP* |
| | | *356.175* | *DIR / PAR RADAR* |
| | | *312.425* | *PAR RADAR* |
| *PLYMOUTH CITY AIRPORT* | CIV AP | 122.6 | TWR |
| | | 133.55 | APP |
| **LISKEARD HELIPORT** | CIV HELIPAD | 129.9 | AG RADIO |
| **BODMIN** | CIV AF | 122.7 | AG RADIO |
| **ST. MAWGAN** | MIL AF | 123.4 | TWR |
| | | 122.1 | TWR / APP |
| | | 125.55 | APP / RAD |
| | | 126.5 | APP / MATZ / LARS |
| | | 125.85 | DIRECTOR / SRE |
| | | 123.3 | DIRECTOR / PAR RADAR |
| | | *241.825* | *TWR* |
| | | *376.625* | *GRND* |
| | | *260.0* | *OPS* |
| | | *357.2* | *APP / LARS* |
| | | *362.3* | *APP* |
| | | *360.55* | *DIR* |
| | | *344.0* | *DIR* |
| | | *336.55* | *PAR RADAR* |
| | | *385.4* | *PAR RADAR* |

# AREA 10A

## AIRFIELDS OF DEVON, CORNWALL & CHANNEL ISLANDS

| STATION | TYPE | FREQUENCY | SERVICE / REMARKS / CALL |
|---|---|---|---|
| **PERRANPORTH** | PRI AF | 119.75 | AG RADIO |
| | | 130.1 | GLIDER OPS |
| **TRURO** | PRI AF | 129.8 | AG RADIO |
| | | 134.05 | CULDROSE APP |
| | | 126.5 | ST MAWGAN APP |
| **PREDANNICK** | MIL AF | 134.05 | CULDROSE APP |
| | | *338.975* | *TWR* |
| | | *370.0* | *TWR* |
| | | *241.95* | *CULDROSE APP* |
| **CULDROSE** | MIL AF | 122.1 | TWR / RAD |
| | | 123.3 | TWR |
| | | 134.05 | APP / RAD / LARS |
| | | *380.225* | *TWR* |
| | | *229.4* | *GRND* |
| | | *372.3* | *OATIS* |
| | | *241.95* | *APP / LARS* |
| | | *339.95* | *RAD* |
| | | *358.7* | *PAR RADAR* |
| | | *259.75* | *PAR RADAR* |
| | HF STN | 5696 KHz | AG RADIO (SSB) |
| **LANDS END (ST JUST)** | CIV AF | 130.7 | TWR / APP |
| *PENZANCE (HELIPORT)* | CIV HELIPORT | 118.1 | TWR |
| *SCILLY ISLES* *(ST MARY'S)* | CIV AP | 123.15 | TWR / APP |
| **TRESCO** | CIV HELIPAD | 130.25 | AG RADIO |
| **SHANWICK RADIO (OCEANIC CONTROL)** | | | |
| NAT A ALL AIRCRAFT | | 3016 KHz | SOUTHERN ROUTES |
| | | 5598 KHz | SOUTHERN ROUTES |
| | | 8906 KHz | SOUTHERN ROUTES |
| | | 13306 KHz | SOUTHERN ROUTES |
| | | 17946 KHz | SOUTHERN ROUTES |
| NAT B A/C REG W. OF 30 W. | | 2899 KHz | NORTH & CEN ROUTES |
| | | 5616 KHz | NORTH & CEN ROUTES |
| | | 8864 KHz | NORTH & CEN ROUTES |
| | | 13291 KHz | NORTH & CEN ROUTES |
| | | 17946 KHz | NORTH & CEN ROUTES |

# AREA 10A

## AIRFIELDS OF DEVON, CORNWALL & CHANNEL ISLANDS

| STATION | TYPE | FREQUENCY | SERVICE / REMARKS / CALL |
|---------|------|-----------|--------------------------|
| NAT C. | A/C REG E OF 30 W. | 2872 KHz | NORTH & CEN ROUTES |
| | | 5649 KHz | NORTH & CEN ROUTES |
| | | 8879 KHz | NORTH & CEN ROUTES |
| | | 11336 KHz | NORTH & CEN ROUTES |
| | | 13306 KHz | NORTH & CEN ROUTES |
| | | 17946 KHz | NORTH & CEN ROUTES |
| NAT D. | A/C OUTSIDE OTS ROUTES | 2971 KHz | POLAR ROUTES |
| | | 4675 KHz | POLAR ROUTES |
| | | 8891 KHz | POLAR ROUTES |
| | | 11279 KHz | POLAR ROUTES |
| | | 13291 KHz | POLAR ROUTES |
| | | 17946 KHz | POLAR ROUTES |
| NAT F. | ALL AIRCRAFT | 3376 KHz | CENTRAL ROUTES |
| | | 6622 KHz | CENTRAL ROUTES |
| | | 8831 KHz | CENTRAL ROUTES |
| | | 13291 KHz | CENTRAL ROUTES |
| | | 17946 KHz | CENTRAL ROUTES |

# AREA 10A

## AIRFIELDS OF THE CHANNEL ISLANDS

| STATION | TYPE | FREQUENCY | SERVICE / REMARKS / CALL |
|---------|------|-----------|--------------------------|
| **ALDERNEY** | CIV AP | 125.35 | TWR |
| | | 125.2 | APP. JERSEY ZONE |
| | | 120.45 | APP. JERSEY ZONE |
| **GUERNSEY** | CIV AP | 119.15 | TWR |
| | | 121.8 | GRND |
| | | 109.4 | ATIS |
| | | 128.65 | APP |
| | | 124.5 | APP / RAD / SRE |
| | | 118.9 | RAD / SRE |
| **JERSEY** | CIV AP | 119.45 | TWR |
| | | 121.9 | GRND |
| | | 112.2 | ATIS. ARRIVALS |
| | | 120.3 | APP / RAD |
| | | 118.55 | ZONE |
| | | 120.45 | ZONE |
| | | 121.6 | FIRE |

# AREA 11

## AIRFIELDS OF NORTHERN IRELAND

| STATION | TYPE | FREQUENCY | SERVICE / REMARKS / CALL |
|---|---|---|---|
| **BELFAST (CITY)** | CIV AP | 130.75 | TWR |
| | | 130.85 | APP |
| | | 134,8 | RAD / SRE |
| **BELFAST (ALDERGROVE)** | CIV AP | 118.3 | TWR |
| | | 121.75 | GRND |
| | | 128.2 | ATIS |
| | | 120.0 | APP |
| | | 120.9 | RAD |
| | | 310.0 | TWR / APP / RAD |
| | | 241.825 | RAF OPS |
| **NEWTONARDS** | CIV AF | 123.5 | G RADIO |
| **DUNDALK** | CIV AF | 122.9 | AG RADIO |
| **LONDONDERRY (EGLINGTON)** | CIV AF | 122.85 | TWR |
| | | 123.625 | APP |
| | | 121.6 | FIRE |
| **ENNISKILLEN (ST ANGELO)** | CIV AF | 123.2 | AG RADIO |

# AREA 11

## AIRFIELDS OF SOUTHERN IRELAND

| STATION | TYPE | FREQUENCY | SERVICE / REMARKS / CALL |
|---|---|---|---|
| **CARRICKFIN** | PRI AF | 129.8 | AG RADIO |
| **SLIGO** | CIV AP | 122.1 | TWR |
| **DONEGAL** | CIV AF | 129.8 | TWR |
| **BELMULLET** | PRI AF | 123.6 | AG RADIO |
| **CONNAUGHT (KNOCK)** | CIV AP | 130.7 | TWR |
| | | 121.9 | GRND |
| **CASTLEBAR** | CIV AF | 122.6 | AG RADIO |
| **CONNEMARA** | PRI AF | 123.0 | AG RADIO |
| **GALWAY (CARNMORE)** | CIV AP | 122.5 | AG RADIO / TWR |
| **INISHMORE** | PRI AF | 123.0 | AG RADIO |

# AREA 11

## AIRFIELDS OF SOUTHERN IRELAND

| STATION | TYPE | FREQUENCY | SERVICE / REMARKS / CALL |
|---|---|---|---|
| **INISHIMAAN** | PRI AF | 123.0 | AG RADIO |
| **INISHEER** | PRI AF | 123.0 | AG RADIO |
| **ABBEYSHRULE** | CIV AF | 122.6 | AG RADIO |
| **CASTLEFORBES** | PRI AF | 130.5 | AG RADIO |
| **TRIM** | PRI AF | 123.3 | AG RADIO |
| **EDENDERRY** | PRI AF | 128.55 | AG RADIO |
| **HACKETSTOWN** | PRI AF | 128.8 | DUBLIN CONTROL |
|  |  | 124.65 | DUBLIN CONTROL |
| *DUBLIN* | CIV AP | 118.6 | TWR |
|  |  | 114.9 | TWR |
|  |  | 121.8 | GRND |
|  |  | 124.525 | ATIS |
|  |  | 121.1 | APP |
|  |  | 119.55 | RAD / DIRECTOR / SRE |
|  |  | 118.5 | DIRECTOR / SRE |
|  |  | 124.65 | DUBLIN CONTROL / ACC |
|  |  | 129.175 | DUBLIN CONTROL / ACC |
| **DUBLIN (WESTON)** | CIV AF | 122.4 | AG RADIO |
|  |  | 118.6 | DUBLIN TWR |
|  |  | 128.0 | DUBLIN CENTRE |
|  |  | 121.1 | DUBLIN DIRECTOR |
| **BALDONNEL** | MIL AF | 123.5 | TWR |
|  |  | 123.1 | GRND |
|  |  | 122.0 | APP |
|  |  | 122.8 | RAD |
|  |  | 122.3 | RAD (DUBLIN MILITARY) |
|  |  | 129.7 | BALDONNEL TALKDOWN |
| **POWERSCOURT** | PRI AF | 123.65 | AG RADIO |
| **SPANISH POINT** | CIV AF | 123.3 | AG RADIO |
|  |  | 124.7 | FIS. SHANNON CONTROL |
| **RATHCOOLE** | PRI AF | 124.7 | SHANNON CONTROL |
| **SHANNON ACC** |  | 131.15 | CORK SECTOR |
|  |  | 135.6 | SOTA SECTOR |
|  |  | 134.275 | SOTA SECTOR |
|  |  | 124.7 | SOTA SECTOR |
|  |  | 132.15 | BABAN/DEVOL SECTOR |

## AIRFIELDS OF SOUTHERN IRELAND

| STATION | TYPE | FREQUENCY | SERVICE / REMARKS / CALL |
|---|---|---|---|
| **SHANNON ACC** | | 127.5 | AS DIRECTED |
| (Continued) | | 121.7 | CENTRE OCEANIC DEL |
| | | 135.225 | SOTA SECTOR |
| **SHANWICK RADIO (OCEANIC CONTROL)** | | | |
| NAT A. | ALL AIRCRAFT | 3016 KHz | SOUTHERN ROUTES |
| | | 5598 KHz | SOUTHERN ROUTES |
| | | 8906 KHz | SOUTHERN ROUTES |
| | | 13306 KHz | SOUTHERN ROUTES |
| | | 17946 KHz | SOUTHERN ROUTES |
| NAT B. | A/C REG W. OF 30 W | 2899 KHz | NORTH & CEN ROUTES |
| | | 5616 KHz | NORTH & CEN ROUTES |
| | | 8864 KHz | NORTH & CEN ROUTES |
| | | 13291 KHz | NORTH & CEN ROUTES |
| | | 17946 KHz | NORTH & CEN ROUTES |
| NAT C. | A/C.REG E OF 30 W. | 2872 KHz | NORTH & CEN ROUTES |
| | | 5649 KHz | NORTH & CEN ROUTES |
| | | 8879 KHz | NORTH & CEN ROUTES |
| | | 11336 KHz | NORTH & CEN ROUTES |
| | | 13306 KHz | NORTH & CEN ROUTES |
| | | 17946 KHz | NORTH & CEN ROUTES |
| NAT D. | A/C OUTSIDE OTS ROUTES | 2971 KHz | POLAR ROUTES |
| | | 4675 KHz | POLAR ROUTES |
| | | 8891 KHz | POLAR ROUTES |
| | | 11279 KHz | POLAR ROUTES |
| | | 13291 KHz | POLAR ROUTES |
| | | 17946 KHz | POLAR ROUTES |
| NAT F. | ALL AIRCRAFT | 3376 KHz | CENTRAL ROUTES |
| | | 6622 KHz | CENTRAL ROUTES |
| | | 8831 KHz | CENTRAL ROUTES |
| | | 13291 KHz | CENTRAL ROUTES |
| | | 17946 KHz | CENTRAL ROUTES |
| **SHANWICK OCEANIC** | AG STATION | 123.95 | OCEANIC CLEARANCE |
| | | 127.65 | OCEANIC CLEARANCE |
| | | 135.525 | AS DIRECTED |
| | | 133.8 | TRACKS BROADCAST |
| ***SHANNON*** | CIV AP | 118.7 | TWR |
| | | 121.8 | GRND |
| | | 130.9 | ATIS |

# AREA 11

## AIRFIELDS OF SOUTHERN IRELAND

| STATION | TYPE | FREQUENCY | SERVICE / REMARKS / CALL |
|---|---|---|---|
| **SHANNON** (Continued) | | 124.7 | SHANNON CONTROL |
| | | 121.4 | APP / RAD DIR |
| | | 120.2 | APP |
| **GOWRAN GRANGE** | PRI AF | 130.4 | AG RADIO (GLIDERS) |
| **BALLYFREE** | PRI AF | 122.9 | AG RADIO |
| **BIRR** | CIV AF | 122.95 | AG RADIO |
| **LIMERICK** | PRI AF | 129.9 | AG RADIO |
| **(COONAGH)** | | 120.2 | SHANNON APP |
| **KILKENNY** | CIV AF | 122.9 | AG RADIO |
| | | 130.4 | GLIDERS |
| **FETHARD** | PRI AF | 123.3 | AG RADIO |
| **CASTLEBRIDGE** | PRI AF | 123.0 | AG RADIO |
| **WATERFORD** | CIV AP | 129.85 | TWR / AFIS |
| **FARRANFORE** | CIV AF | 122.6 | TWR |
| **BANTRY** | PRI AF | 122.4 | AG RADIO |
| **KERRY** | CIV AP | 124.1 | TWR |
| | | 121.6 | GRND |
| **CORK** | CIV AP | 119.3 | TWR |
| | | 121.7 | TWR |
| | | 120.925 | ATIS |
| | | 121.8 | GRND |
| | | 119.9 | APP |
| | | 118.8 | RAD / SRE |
| **KILBRITTAIN** | PRI AF | 122.9 | AG RADIO |

# COMMUNICATION COMMON FREQUENCIES

| FREQUENCY | USAGE |
|---|---|
| 118.0 | AIR TO AIR |
| 121.1 | RAF TOWERS & APPROACH (STANDBY} |
| 121.5 | INTERNATIONAL EMERGENCY |
| 121.6 | FIRE & RESCUE |
| 123.1 | INTERNATIONAL SAR |
| 123.3 | RAF RADARS (STANDBY) |
| 125.05 | SOUTHEND AIR PAGENTS |
| 129.7 | TRINITY HOUSE HELICOPTERS |
| 129.9 | UK BALLOONS (COMMON FREQUENCY) |
| 130.1 | UK GLIDERS (COMMON FREQUENCY) |
| 130.125 | UK GLIDERS (COMMON FREQUENCY) |
| 130.4 | UK GLIDERS (COMMON FREQUENCY) |
| 131.8 | AIR TO AIR (INTERNATIONAL COMMON FREQUENCY) |
| 240.4 | AIR TO AIR REFUELLING |
| 243.45 | RED ARROWS DISPLAY TEAM |
| 243.0 | NATO INTERNATIONAL EMERGENCY |
| 244.0 | UK SAR |
| 252.8 | NATO SAR (TRAINING) |
| 252.9 | BRITISH ARMY |
| 255.1 | ARMY AIR |
| 257.8 | NATO TWRS. (COMMON FREQUENCY STANDBY) |
| 259.7 | NASA. (SPACE SHUTTLE) |
| 282.8 | NATO (SAR TRAINING) |
| 285.85 | BOULMER RESCUE (AG) |
| 294.8 | AIR TO AIR REFUELLING |
| 296.8 | SPACE SHUTTLE (VOICE) |
| 297.8 | RESCUE |
| 303.0 | AIR TO AIR REFUELLING |
| 306.5 | AIR TO AIR REFUELLING |
| 316.35 | AIR TO AIR REFUELLING (USAF) |
| 317.2 | AIR TO AIR REFUELLING (USAF) |
| 326.9 | AIR TO AIR REFUELLING |
| 344.0 | NATO RADARS (COMMON FREQUENCY STANDBY) |
| 344.1 | AIR TO AIR REFUELLING |
| 362.3 | NATO APPROACHES (COMMON FREQUENCY STANDBY) |
| 380.8 | AIR TO AIR REFUELLING |
| 385.4 | NATO PAR RADARS (COMMON FREQUENCY STANDBY) |
| 394.8 | AIR TO AIR REFUELLING |

# AMENDMENT PAGE

# AIRCRAFT RECOGNITION SECTION

### Aerospatiale/BAC Concorde
Four turbojet supersonic airliner
**Basic data for Concorde 102**
**Powerplant:** Four Rolls-Royce/SNECMA Olympus 593 (reheat) of 38,050lb st
**Span:** 83ft 10in (25.47m)
**Length:** 203ft 9in (62.10m)
**Max cruise:** 1,336mph (2,179km/h)
**Passengers:** 128 plus three crew
**First aircraft flown:** 2  March 1969
**Production:** Two prototypes, two pre-production and 16 production aircraft
**Recent/current service with:** Air France (seven) British Airways (seven)
**Recognition:** Underwing mounted engines in two double nacelles. Slender, low slung
  delta wing. Narrow fuselage with pointed nose that droops for landing. No tailplane,
  angular fin and rudder. Very tall undercarriage
**Variants:** None amongst the aircraft in service. Preliminary work on a successor is in
  hand with Aerospatiale and BAe


### Antonov An124 'Condor'
Four turbofan long-range airliner
**Powerplant:** Four Lotarev D18T turbofans of 51,590lb st
**Span:** 240ft 6in (73.30m)
**Length:** 228ft (69.50m)
**Max cruise:** 537mph (865km/h)
**First aircraft flown:** 26  December 1982
Similar to the C-5 Galaxy it has an upward-hinged nose section and a rear-loading
  ramp. Approximately 20 have been built of which 15 are believed to have been
  delivered to Aeroflot


### Aerospatiale-Aeritalia ATR72
Twin turboprop regional airliner
**Basic data for Avions de Transport Regional ATR72**
**Powerplant:** Two Pratt & Whitney Canada PW12 of 2,400shp
**Span:** 88ft 9in (27.05m)
**Length:** 89ft 2in (27.17m)
**Max cruise:** 326mph (524km/h) at 18,000ft
**Passengers:** Up to 74 plus 2 crew
**First aircraft flown:** 27 October 1988
**Recent/current service with:** Transport Aérien Transrégional, American Eagle, Britair
  and Karair
**Recognition:** High-set wing with slim engines projecting forward and below the wing.
  Circular section fuselage with large undercarriage fairings under the centre section.
  Large swept fin and rudder with two angle changes on the forward edge. Tailplane
  set near to the top of the fin.
**Variants:** The ATR72 is a stretched variant of the ART42. It is the first airliner with a
  carbonfibre wing box. An ATR82 with a further stretch for 82 passengers is under
  consideration as is an ATR72 Advanced with PW130 turboprops for 'hot and high'
  operations

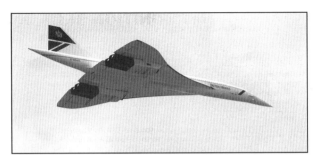

An Aerospatiale/BAC Concorde in British Airways service. *Daniel J. March*

The four-engined AN124 is in service with Aeroflot and Heavylift. *Peter R. March*

The ATR72 shows considerable fuselage 'stretch' over the ATR42. *Peter R. March*

## Boeing 747

Four turbofan long-range 'Jumbo' airliner
**Basic data for Boeing 747-400**
**Powerplant:** Four Rolls-Royce RB211-524G turbofans of 2.58kN
**Span:** 210ft (64.30m)
**Length:** 231ft 10in (70.70m)
**Max cruise:** 584mph (940km/h)
**Passengers:** Up to 660 plus crew
**First aircraft flown:** 9 February 1969
**Recent/current service with:** Most of the world's major airlines
**Recognition:** Underwing mounted engines in four separate nacelles. Swept, low-set
  wing which narrow towards the tips. Oval, wide body fuselage with a distinctive
  raised fuselage forward of the wing incorporating the cabin and flight deck. Tall,
  swept fin with a fuselage mounted tailplane below the rudder
**Variants:** There are 15 current variants of the 747

## Boeing 757

Twin turbofan medium range airliner
**Basic data for Boeing 757200**
**Powerplant:** Two Rolls-Royce RB211-535E4 of 40,100lb st
**Span:** 124ft 10in (38.05m)
**Length:** 155ft 3in (47.32m)
**Max cruise:** 569mph (916km/h)
**Passengers:** 239 plus two crew
**First aircraft flown:** 19 February 1982
**Recent/current service with:** 31 airlines
**Recognition:** Engines in nacelles under the wings. A long, circular, narrow-body
  fuselage with swept, low-set wings at the mid-way point. A pronounced lower
  fuselage bulge for the undercarriage fairing. A tall, swept fin and rudder with a swept
  tailplane on either side of the rear fuselage below the fin
**Variants:** The Boeing 757PF (Package Freighter) has a forward cargo door and a
  windowless fuselage. The first aircraft of an order for 20 was delivered to United
  Parcel Service in September 1987. The 757M is Combi with side cargo door.
  Alternative powerplant is the Pratt & Whitney PW2037/PW2040

Boeing 747-400 of Cathay Pacific showing the familiar winglets. *Peter R. March*

A Boeing 757-277 of Monarch Airlines. *Peter R. March*

## Boeing 737-300/400/500

Twin turbofan medium-range airliner

**Basic data for Boeing 737-300**

**Powerplant:** Two CFM56-3B-2 turbofans of 22,000lb st

**Span:** 94ft 9in (28.88m)

**Length:** 109ft 7in (33.4m)

**Max cruise:** 558mph (899km/h)

**Passengers:** Up to 149 plus 2 crew

**First aircraft flown:** 24 February 1984 (300), 19 February 1988 (400), 30 June 1989 (500)

**Recent/current service with:** Aer Lingus, Air France, American West, Ansett AL, Asiana, Australian AL, Braathens, British Airways, British Midland, Continental, Dan Air, Germania, KLM, Lufthansa, Maersk, Monarch, MIS, Sabena, Southwest AL, TEA, Thai, United and US Air

**Recognition:** Large engines, with oval nacelles, mounted under and forward of the swept wings. Circular fuselage with wings set in the lower section. Tall, angular, slightly swept fin and rudder with a pronounced dorsal fin. Swept tailplane set on the rear fuselage at the base of the rudder

**Variants:** 400 series has increased length of 119ft 7in (36.4m) to carry up to 168 passengers, with two CFM56-3C turbofans of 23,500lb st. First delivery was September 1988. 500 series has a shortened fuselage of 101ft 9in (31m), with two CFM56-3-B1 turbofans of 20,000lb st. Carries up to 122 passengers in the all economy version, or 108 in mixed-class configuration. First delivery was February to South West Airlines


## Dornier Do228

Twin turboprop commuter airline

**Basic data for Dornier Do228 Series 200**

**Powerplant:** Two Garrett TPE 3315252D turboprops rated at 776shp

**Span:** 55ft 7in (16.94m)

**Length:** 54ft 3in (16.54m)

**Max cruise:** 230mph (370km/h)

**Passengers:** 19 plus 2 crew

**First aircraft flown:** 28 March 1981 (Series 100) and 9 May 1981 (Series 200)

**Recent/current service with:** 50 airlines worldwide

**Recognition:** Small turboprops mounted on the leading edge of the 'new technology' wing which has a straight trailing edge and curved leading edge with pointed wing-tip. The square, slab-sided fuselage is positioned below the wing. Forward of the cockpit the flat-bottomed nose is shaped downwards to give a 'drooped' appearance. The angular fin and rudder has a large dorsal fillet extending to the end of the wing fairing. The flat tailplane is mounted below the rudder, extending beyond the fuselage cone. The main undercarriage retracts into lower fuselage fairing

**Variants:** Series 100 has a fuselage 49ft 3in (15.01m) for 15 passengers, the Series 200 has a 5ft (1.52m) longer fuselage for 19 passengers. The 203F freighter version has a 2,300kg payload. The 30-seat Do328 with PW119s is now in production

Boeing 737-300 of British Midland. *Peter R. March*

The Dornier Do228-200 has a square section fuselage and a crescent-shaped wing profile. *Peter R. March*

## Lockheed TriStar

Three turbofan long-range airliner
**Basic data for TriStar 100**
**Powerplant:** Three Rolls-Royce RB211-22B of 42,000lb st
**Span:** 155ft 4in (47.35m)
**Length:** 177ft 8in (54.15m)
**Max cruise:** 575mph (925km/h)
**Passengers:** Maximum of 330 plus three crew
**First aircraft flown:** 17 November 1970
**Recent/current service with:** 22 airlines worldwide
**Recognition:** Two engines in underwing nacelles and one engine mounted on top of
the fuselage forward of the swept fin, with the jet efflux below the rudder through the
tail cone. Circular wide-body fuselage with low-set swept wings at mid-way point.
Swept tailplane low-set either side of the rear fuselage below the fin
**Variants:** TriStar Series 1, 100 and 200 have powerplant and internal differences only.
The major variant is the longer L1011-500 (first flown 16 October 1978) which has
extended wings to give a span of 164ft 4in (50.09m), 13ft 6in (4.12m) shorter
fuselage (to 164ft 2in [50.04m]) and other internal modifications

## McDonnell Douglas MD-80

Twin turbofan short/medium range airliner
**Basic data for MD-81**
**Powerplant:** Two Pratt & Whitney JT8D209 turbofans of 19,250lb st
**Span:** 107ft 10in (32.87m)
**Length:** 147ft 11in (45.08m)
**Max cruise:** 574mph (924km/h) at 27,000ft
**Passengers:** Maximum 172 plus 2 crew
**First aircraft flown:** 18 October 1979 (MD80)
**Recent/current service with:** 45 airlines worldwide
**Recognition:** Engines mounted on the sides of the rear fuselage forward of the swept
fin and rudder. Low-set swept wings which taper towards the tips. Non-swept inboard
trailing edges and 10in taller fin. Narrow body, circular fuselage considerably
extended forward of the wings compared with the earlier DC9 series
**Variants:** Originally known as the Super 80, the MD-80 series has these sub types:
MD-81 as above
MD-82 more powerful JT8D217 turbofans of 20,850lb st
MD-83 higher all up weight and payload/range
MD-87 shorter fuselage length 130ft 6in (39.73m). JT8D 217 turbofans (20,850lb st)
and carries 130 passengers
MD-88 longer fuselage length 147ft 11in (45.08m) and JT8D217 turbofans (20,850lb st)

A Lockheed TriStar of All Nippon Airways. *Peter R. March*

The MD-81 development of the DC9 has a stretched fuselage. *Daniel J. March*

## McDonnell Douglas MD-11

Three turbofan long-range airliner

**Basic data for MD-11**

**Powerplant:** Three General Electric CF680C2 of 61,500lb st

**Span:** 169ft 6in (57.66m)

**Length:** 200ft 10in (61.21m)

**Max cruise:** 578mph (930km/h)

**Passengers:** Maximum 405 plus 2 crew

**First aircraft flown:** 10 January 1990

**Recent/current service with:** Entered service with Finnair in December 1990 and American Airlines early in 1991

**Recognition:** Two engines in underwing nacelles close to fuselage, one engine mounted on the fin above the fuselage with a straight-through exhaust pipe to the rear. A circular, wide-body fuselage with low-set, swept wings. Tailplane mid-set on the rear fuselage below the fin, Winglets are fitted.

**Variants:** The basic MD-11 has a DC-10 Srs 30 fuselage lengthened by 18ft 9in (5.71m). Combi and freighter versions are in production. Airlines will also be able to specify Rolls-Royce RB211-524L Trent turbofans as as option


## Shorts 360

Twin turboprop regional airliner

**Basic data for Shorts 360**

**Powerplant:** Two Pratt & Whitney PT6A67R of 1,424shp

**Span:** 74ft (22.76m)

**Length:** 70ft 6in (21.49m)

**Max cruise:** 242mph (390km/h)

**Passengers:** 36 plus 2 crew

**Recent/current service with:** Aer Lingus Commuter, Air UK, Business Express, CCAir, Formosa, Hazelton, Jersey European, Loganair, Manx Airlines, Philippine together with 12 US commuter airlines

**Recognition:** A refined development of the Shorts 330 with a 3ft (0.91m) longer fuselage forward of the wing and a distinctive, tall, single fin and rudder, set on top of the tapered upswept rear fuselage. The wing-shape, forward fuselage, bracing struts, retractable undercarriage and powerplants are similar to the Shorts 330

**Variants:** Externally all versions are similar. The 360-300 has P&W Canada PT6A-67R turboprops driving six-blade propellers and internal improvements

The new MD-11 is longer than the DC-10 and has winglets. *Peter R. March*

A Shorts 360 of Jersey European. *Peter R. March*

## British Aerospace BAe RJ (Regional Jet)

Four turbofan short-range airliner

**Basic data for BAe146**

**Powerplant:** Four Avco Lycoming ALF502R-5 of 6,970lb st

**Span:** 85ft 5in (26.04m)

**Length:** 85ft 10in (26.16m)

**Max cruise:** 482mph (776km/h)

**Passengers:** 93 plus 2 crew, 300 series — 112 in high density mode

**First aircraft flown:** 3 September 1981

**Recent/current service with:** 40 airlines worldwide

**Recognition:** Underwing mounted engines in four nacelles. Slightly swept wings mounted on top of the fuselage, drooping towards the wing tips. Distinctive trailing edge wing fillets. The fuselage is circular in section with bulges on the lower side to accommodate the undercarriage. The rectangular fin and rudder is slightly swept with a T-tailplane mounted on the top of the fin. There are sideways opening airbrakes below the rudder

**Variants:** The initial BAe146-100 was followed by the stretched 200 series and by a further stretched version, the 300. The QT (Quiet Trader) is offered as a freight version of the series 100/200. Other versions announced or in production include the QC (Quick Change) and RJ70, RJ80 and RJ100

## Airbus A320/321

Twin turbofan medium range airliner

**Basic data for Airbus A320200**

**Powerplant:** Two CFM 56-5 turbofans of 25,000lb st

**Span:** 111ft 3in (33.91m)

**Length:** 123ft 3in (37.57m)

**Max cruise:** 561mph (903km/h)

**Passengers:** 179 maximum plus 2 crew

**First aircraft flown:** 22 February 1987

**Recent/current service with:** First delivery to Air France on 18 April 1988 and to British Airways on 20 April 1988. Other operators include Air Inter, Air Malta, Alitalia, Conair, Iberia, Indian Airlines, Lufthansa and Northwest AL

**Recognition:** Underwing mounted engines in nacelles protruding forward of the wings. Circular narrow body fuselage tapering upwards towards the tail. Low-set, swept wings of narrow chord with three tailing edge fairings. Tall, swept fin and rudder set forward of tail cone. Swept tailplane with dihedral

**Variants:** Announced in 1989 the A321 has a 22ft 9in (7m) stretched fuselage, 13ft (4.3m) being forward of the wing

## Airbus A340

Four turbofan-engined very long-range airliner

**Powerplant:** Four General Electric SNECMA CFM-56-5C turbofans of 31,200lb st

**Span:** 192ft 5in ((58.6m)

**Length:** 194ft 10in (59.4m), Series 200 208ft 10in (63.6m)

**Passengers:** 283 plus crew on Virgin Atlantic

**First aircraft flown:** 1993

**Recent/current service with:** Virgin Atlantic and c20 other international airlines have the A340 on order

**Recognition:** Has distinctive winglets on the wingtips.

A BAe146QC of TNT. *Peter R. March*

The first Airbus A320 entered service with British Airways in 1988. *Peter R. March*

Virgin Atlantic received its first A340s in late 1993. *Peter March*

**Fokker 50**
Twin turboprop regional transport
**Basic data for Fokker 50**
**Powerplant:** Two Pratt & Whitney Canada PW125B turboprops of 2,500shp
**Span:** 95ft 2in (29.00m)
**Length:** 82ft 8in (25.25m)
**Max cruise:** 332mph (535km/h) at 20,000ft
**Passengers:** Maximum 58 plus 2 crew
**First aircraft flown:** 28 December 1985
**Recent/current service with:** Aer Lingus, Ansett Transport Ind, Austrian, Busy Bee, Crossair, KLM, Maersk, Philippine AL and SAS
**Recognition:** Little different from the F27500 from which it is derived. Twin turboprops set below the high straight wings. A slender, oval section fuselage with a pointed nose and tail. A tall fin and rudder with large dorsal extension. The small tailplane is set either side of the base of the rudder. Fokker 50 has smaller rectangular windows than F27 500

**British Aerospace Jetstream**
Twin turboprop commuter airliner
**Basic data for Jetstream 31**
**Powerplant:** Two flat-rated Garrett TPE331-10 turboprops of 940shp
**Span:** 52ft 0in (15.85m)
**Length:** 47ft 2in (14.36m)
**Max cruise:** 303mph (488km/h)
**Passengers:** 18 plus one/two crew
**First aircraft flown:** 28 March 1980; the original Handley Page Jetstream was flown on 18 August 1967
**Recent/current service with:** Some 15 airlines worldwide
**Recognition:** Twin turboprops mounted above and forward of the low-set wings. Circular fuselage with a long, pointed nose forward of the cockpit. Swept, tall fin and rudder with a triangular ventral extension. Circular cabin windows and a passenger door aft of the port wing
**Variants:** The original Handley Plage Jetstream has Turbomeca Astazou XIV turboprops which are more slender and extend further forward of the wing, with a distinctive long spinner. The Super 31 has uprated engines — Garrett TPE331-12 turboprops of 1,020shp, improved cabin and increased max take-off weight. The 41 is a stretched version (63ft 2in/19.25m) with Garrett TPE331-14 of 1,500shp turboprops

A Fokker 50 of Aer Lingus. *Brian S. Strickland*

A BAe Jetstream 31 of Birmingham European. *Peter R. March*

### Cessna 172 Skyhawk

All-metal four-seat piston engined touring/training aircraft
**Basic data for Cessna 172P Skyhawk II**
**Powerplant:** One 160hp Lycoming O320D2J piston engine
**Span:** 35ft 10in (10.92m)
**Length:** 26ft 11in (8.20m)
**Max cruise:** 138mph (222km/h)
**Passengers:** Pilot plus three passengers
**First aircraft flown:** 1955
**Recognition:** high-wing monoplane with single thick wing braces under leading edge. Slightly tapered wings with squared tips. Tricycle undercarriage often featuring wheel spats. Swept fin and rudder with small dorsal fillet at front of fin. Tailplane set low at rear extremity
**Variants:** Some 13 variants of the Cessna 172 exist


### Cessna Citation

Twin turbofan executive transport
**Basic data for Cessna 550 Citation II**
**Powerplant:** Two 2,500lb (1,135kg) Pratt & Whitney JT15D4 turbofans
**Span:** 51ft 8in (15.75m)
**Length:** 47ft 2in (14.38m)
**Max cruise:** 443mph (713km/h)
**Passengers:** Pilot and up to nine passengers
**First aircraft flown:** 15 September 1969
**Recognition:** Low-wing monoplane with straight leading edge wings. The Citation II has a fillet at leading edge wing roots. Twin engines are mounted aft half way up the fuselage. Moderately swept fin and rudder with dihedral tailplane set on fin. Large glass area to front cockpit
**Variants:** Cessna 500 Citation — first model; four cabin windows each side; 501 Citation I — longer span wings with uprated engines; 550 Citation II — modified wing, longer fuselage, six cabin windows each side; 551 Citation II/SP — for single pilot operation; 650 Citation III — longer range, more powerful Garrett TFE7313B100S turbofans; 560 Citation V — longer fuselage 550 with seven cabin windows each side

Cessna 172. *Daniel J. March*

Cessna Citation III. *Peter R. March*

## Piper PA-28 Cherokee series

Single-engined four-seat light aircraft

**Basic data for Piper PA28181 Archer II**

**Powerplant:** One 180hp Lycoming O360A4M piston engine

**Span:** 35ft 0in (10.67m)

**Length:** 23ft 9in (7.26m)

**Max cruise:** 148mph (239km/h)

**Passengers:** Pilot plus three passengers

**First aircraft flown:** 10 January 1960

**Recognition:** Low-wing monoplane. Wings, with pronounced dihedral, of equal chord with rounded tips. Outer wings on later models were tapered. Fillet at front wing root. Fixed tricycle undercarriage, with mainwheel spats. Swept fin and rudder with dorsal fillet. Low-set oblong tailplane. Trim options included Standard, Custom and Super Custom

**Variants:** Numerous


## Piper PA-38-112 Tomahawk

Single-engine two-seat aerobatic trainer

**Basic data for Piper PA-38-112 Tomahawk**

**Powerplant:** One Lycoming O235L2C piston engine

**Span:** 34ft 0in (10.36m)

**Length:** 23ft 2in (7.04m)

**Max cruise:** 126mph (202km/h)

**Passengers:** Two side-by-side seats

**First aircraft flown:** 1977

**Production:** 2,519

**Recognition:** Low-wing monoplane with fixed tricycle undercarriage. Tailplane mounted high on the fin. Ne rear fuselage decking behind cabin which has 360° visibility. Wing of equal chord and rounded tips. Oblong tailplane with small cut out at fin

**Variants:** none

Piper Cherokee. *Peter R. March*

Piper Tomahawk. *Peter R. March*

## Bell 206 JetRanger/206L LongRanger

General purpose commercial helicopter

**Basic data for Bell Model 206B JetRanger III**

**Powerplant:** One 420shp Allison 250-C20J turboshaft

**Main rotor diameter:** 33ft 4in (10.16m)

**Length:** 31ft 2in (9.5m)

**Max cruise:** 134mph (216km/h)

**Passengers:** Pilot plus up to four passengers

**First aircraft flown:** 10 January 1966

**Recognition:** Enclosed turboshaft above cabin. Large glazed cabin windows and
pointed nose, Tail boom has small tailplane half way along the empennage and swept
dorsal/ventral fin. Twin blade main rotor. Skid undercarriage. LongRanger has plates
at ends of tailplane

**Variants:** 206A — original production version with 317shp Allison 250C18A; 206B
JetRanger II — with 400shp Allison 250C20; 206B JetRanger III — with 420shp
Allison 250C20J; 206L LongRanger — stretched cabin, increased seating capacity;
OH-58 Kiowa — military variant of the JetRanger with 420shp Allison T63-A-720

Bell JetRanger. *Peter R. March*